S0-AJE-478

INTRODUCTION

In planning the publishing of *Volume 10* many options were considered. We decided on the following; a new Israel Sack brochure which we designed and printed for them showing their establishment of fine American antiques, as part of our introduction. For those of you who have never visited Israel Sack, I recommend that a trip to New York would be worth your time.

Over the years some of the most enlightening and enjoyable reading every month has been the introduction of *The Magazine Antiques* with an essay by Wendell Garrett. I have selected forty-eight of those essays, starting with May 1973, to include in this volume. They are labeled *The Best of Wendell Garrett.* This is not to infer that the rest of Wendell's essays are not great, they are. The forty-eight selected particularly caught my fancy because they cover life in Colonial America. I believe you will enjoy my selection. I asked Harold Sack for his comments on Wendell's essays, and have placed them preceding the essays.

I have also included the following three articles: *Regionalism in Early American Tea Tables,* by Albert Sack; *American Roundabout Chairs,* by Harold Sack and Deanne Levison; and *Queen Anne and Chippendale Armchairs in America,* by Harold Sack and Deanne Levison.

Brochures forty-five, forty-six, forty-seven and forty-eight, with a complete Index for the ten volumes, complete *Volume 10* with over 200 pages in color. This brings the set to over 3,000 pages, with 700 pages in color, showing over 5,000 antiques of American decorative arts, especially edited and annotated for accuracy and completeness. Showing and identifying the finest examples of the art of the Colonial and early Federal Periods, many of these superb examples have appeared nowhere else in print.

I know you will find these volumes a source of pleasure and a valuable tool for research and reference, as I have.

I commend them to you.

Joseph H Hennage

Joseph H. Hennage
Publisher

Special thanks to Sandra Brant, publisher of *The Magazine Antiques,* for permission to include the forty-eight essays by Wendell Garrett and the three articles by Albert Sack, Harold Sack and Deanne Levison. The Magazine Antiques, 575 Broadway, New York, NY 10012.

Library of Congress Catalogue Card Number 76-10283
International Standard Book Number 0-918712-09-2
Printed in the United States of America

Israel Sack, Inc. is more than a company—it is a tradition. That tradition is rooted in the principles and record of its founder, Israel Sack, and carried on by his three sons.

The first element in that tradition is its belief in the importance of our American artistic heritage. No man has been more identified with the development of interest in Americana than Israel Sack, and no firm has been more responsible in placing great examples of Americana in public or private collections than Israel Sack, Inc.

The second element in that tradition is the enviable reputation for personal and professional integrity maintained by Israel Sack, Inc. throughout the century. Every piece sold by our firm reflects the standards of authenticity and quality that are identified with the Sack name.

The third element in that tradition is the leadership the Sack family has maintained in the developing scholarship and identification of American furniture contributions. Its mission was to prove that American craftsmen were creators, not imitators—that in beauty achieved by fine line and form rather than embellishments, American artisans had no equals. To further this goal, Israel Sack, Inc. has forged a role of educational leadership. Its identification with the American sections of our major museums, as well as the Diplomatic Re-

ception Rooms in the State Department and the White House, is significant. The Sack family has donated galleries to the Metropolitan Museum, The Art Institute of Chicago, The Hood Museum at Dartmouth and a room at New England College. The Sack Foundation has supported, or financed, many museum exhibitions, publications and research projects. Members of this firm, as well as our consultant, Deanne Levison, are on the boards of various museums, and all have given hundreds of lectures and written major articles on various phases of Americana.

"Fine Points of Furniture, Early American" by Albert Sack and "American Treasure Hunt" by Harold Sack are widely read books on this field. We maintain a comprehensive library and employ a full-time librarian.

There are several reasons why purchasing an American antique from Israel Sack, Inc. is a prudent investment in lasting pleasure and assured value.

1. Sole ownership:

We own our entire inventory. When you buy from us, you are buying our faith in the object by the investment of our own capital.

2. Performance:

While we stress pleasure and equity as the soundest basis for collecting, the record of increases in value of

items purchased from us has been dramatic and rewarding. The good will maintained with former clients, and our ability to repurchase objects they have bought from us in the past at strong prevailing prices affords us a choice source of supply not available to our competitors.

3. Fair Pricing:

New York is unique in drawing on a national market. This enables us to attract a broader potential market and generate greater volume of annual business, proportionately neutralizing any effect of a larger overhead. An object must be graded from a broad spectrum in determining its value. Our spectrum encompasses the many objects we have observed of a particular category. One must know the relative standing of a piece within its category to evaluate it properly. Our policy has always been to offer sound values based on broad experience.

4. Expertise:

The depth of experience of the principals of Israel Sack, Inc. encompasses well over 100 years of cumulative experience in this field. The expertise of Deanne Levison, which is widely recognized, has proven an invaluable asset to our firm. Integrity, plus experience, form a vital combination for successful expertise.

5. Publication:

Most items purchased appear or have appeared in volumes entitled "American Antiques from Israel Sack Collection". This consists to date of nine volumes and are published by Highland House Publishers, Inc. These volumes are in most museum and collector's libraries and are accepted and quoted in the literature and scholarship of the field.

6. Authenticity:

Each sale is accompanied by a comprehensive invoice. The invoice includes a decorative arts description of the article, its place of origin, circa and an unconditional guarantee that the object is guaranteed as described. This assurance is backed by the proven record and stability of Israel Sack, Inc.

7. Conservation:

Sack Conservation Company is the outgrowth of the need of Israel Sack, Inc. for proper conservation of the objects in our own inventory. The professionalism and level of expertise at Sack Conservation Company is of the highest quality and its services are available to anyone wishing to preserve and conserve fine antique furniture. A free brochure is available.

We consider education a paramount function of a dealer. It is always a special pleasure to offer the benefits of our experience and expertise to collectors of all levels. Appointments are not necessary. We welcome your visit at any time.

Photographs by JAMES L. CONZO

Harold Sack

As an artist paints a picture—a touch here, a touch there, one sees a picture develop before one's eyes. A landscape, a mountain, a terrain emerges with the touch that opens one's mind to a picture created that stimulates the mind, the imagination and the stream of thoughts that somehow touch upon one's experiences in life and one's perceptions.

It is just such a touch that in each short essay Wendell Garrett gives us a perception of life in Colonial America that includes the politics, social background, historical perspective and artistic climate that illuminates the period in which our craftsmen worked.

The picture painted by Wendell Garrett is unique and can only have been crafted by one whose experience and background in all these fields have brought our Colonial period into focus.

Harold Sack

The Best *of* Wendell Garrett

Antiques

THE STUDY OF American furniture, and of English furniture, as a branch of cultural history worthy of serious scholarly investigation is astonishingly recent. Nothing of importance in American furniture research predates the seminal work of Irving W. Lyon in the early 1890's on the furniture of colonial New England. Since then a sizable though largely undistinguished shelf of books has been published on the subject of American furniture—considered by region, by period, and by type. But the few truly significant pieces of work have tended to be somewhat ephemeral in nature: that is, they have appeared serially in periodicals or in the comprehensive catalogues of institutions, exhibitions, and auctions. This bleak and somewhat sketchy picture of American furniture history has brightened recently with the appearance of a few major works and with the knowledge that others are far along in preparation. And the formation in London of the Furniture History Society in October 1964 with the subsequent publication of its annual journal, *Furniture History*, has made the study of furniture irrefutably worthy of scholarly respect (see ANTIQUES, April 1971, p. 542). With this issue *The Magazine* ANTIQUES is launching the annual publication in the spring of a number devoted exclusively to American furniture, which it is fervently hoped will encourage further research while disseminating knowledge of recent findings.

The reader of these articles will find here samples of the rich complexity and contrariness of American life, something of the full variety and vast range of our social and cultural institutions. Furniture is a three-dimensional document which can and should be read: even though it lacks the vivid precision of a literary tradition, by its iridescence, its ability to reflect the shifting lights and colors of its age, it hints at the concord of opposing notes which makes our tradition. These objects are not mere relics but *res Americana*, the matter of America.

From the beginning America was a haven, a refuge, a land of the second chance to which came, as Stephen Vincent Benét has so eloquently reminded us, "the disinherited, the dispossessed." Disinherited and dispossessed of worldly goods they were, for the most part, but the first settlers were heirs nevertheless of all that England was and meant in the seventeenth century. Well might they have said with Richard Rich, whose *Newes from Virginia* is one of the earliest poems about the New World: "Let England know our willingness, for that our work is good/We hope to plant a nation, where none before hath stood." That hope was shared by the others who soon joined and intermingled with the English—Scots and Scotch-Irish, the Dutch, the Swedes, the French Huguenots, the Germans, the Negroes who came as slaves, and in the nineteenth century by the Irish, Germans, Scandinavians, Italians, Poles, Russians, Jews, and others. Uprooted and transplanted to the New World, all these brought their strength not only of body and heart, but of mind and culture as well, and blended into the American pattern. By some alchemy, out of the mixing of inheritance, environment, and historical experience, came a distinctive national character.

The "American Farmer," Jean de Crèvecoeur, saw this at the very beginning of our national history, and in his famous letters drew the American in lines that are clear even today. Americans, he found, built upon their European inheritance something that was clearly part of Western civilization, yet unique. In time they themselves came to appreciate the fact that there had emerged a distinctively American mind and character. They were a people of paradox with their polite rapacity, their erosive buoyancy, their collective individualism, their bourgeois aristocracy. The same was true of their arts—as seen in the Puritan aesthetic, "ostentatious austerity"; and the Quaker aesthetic, "of the best sort but plain."

And in American furniture, even though there were many diverse strains and contradictory influences at work, a recognizable, coherent "American style" did eventually crystallize. It was the work of regional craftsmen that combined quality, utility, and beauty, at times to an astonishing degree, into what might be called today "artisan mannerism." It was a style, in the widest sense of the word, of simultaneous imitation and distortion, slavishly aping European high style yet deliberately exaggerating it. It assumed a precarious balance between affectation and overcompensation on the one hand and subtlety and elegance on the other. Artisan mannerism reflected a feeling of insecurity and individuality on the part of the American craftsmen, men often inadequately trained as a result of the disintegrating apprenticeship system; and in time with the coming of nineteenth-century mass production the style became self-conscious and hackneyed.

The American furniture presented here should tell us something about the people who settled these shores, the hopes and aspirations that inspired them, and the way their new environment molded their character and their traditions. It should tell us something of the wonderful diversity of the American social scene: the mixture of races and people, cultures and religions, which somehow fused into a unity, vindicating the national motto, *E pluribus unum.*

Wendell Garrett

Antiques

The god who gave us life,
gave us liberty at the same time:
the hand of force may destroy,
but cannot disjoin them.

A Summary View of the Rights of British America, 1774.

I have sworn upon the altar of god,
eternal hostility against every form
of tyranny over the mind of man.

Letter to Dr. Benjamin Rush, September 23, 1800.

THOMAS JEFFERSON was quite beyond any of his contemporaries—Benjamin Franklin perhaps excepted—in the breadth of his mind, his studies, and his skills. Intellectually he exemplified more conspicuously than any of his fellows the liberal and humane spirit, the incessant scientific curiosity and zeal for universal knowledge, and the fundamental belief in the powers of human intelligence which characterized the Enlightenment. Of all the founding fathers, he was the most philosophical, and of all the statesmen of the eighteenth century, the most advanced. The historian Henry Steele Commager has called Jefferson "the central figure in American history and—if freedom and democracy survive our generation—he may yet prove to be the central figure in modern history."

No one has yet explored fully the richness of this seemingly inexhaustible mind and extraordinarily versatile man. He looms tall and noble, casting a long shadow over the whole landscape of American history. This inveterate intellectual was a veritable titan of learning: he was a scientist and inventor; he was a bibliophile, collecting not one but two of the greatest private libraries in early America; he was a lawyer and collector of law reports; he was a classical scholar and Biblical student; he was a philologist and mastered six languages; he was a farmer, experimenting endlessly with crops and stock; he was a horticulturist, compiling a garden book of lasting value; he was the greatest American architect of his day; he was something of a musician, playing the violin and collecting musicians around himself; and he sponsored far-reaching education reforms and founded the University of Virginia. How he found time for it all, even in a life of eighty-three years, is a matter of perpetual astonishment and one of the mysteries of history. "He was a miser of his time," his grandson Thomas Jefferson Randolph once said, and went on to explain: "He said in his last illness, that the sun had not caught him in bed for fifty years."

For forty years, from 1769 to 1809, Jefferson was a towering figure in American politics, passing through the offices of Virginia legislator, representative to the Continental Congress, governor of his state, ambassador to France, secretary of state, vice-president, and finally, from 1801 to 1809, president of the United States. When he completed his second presidential term, he fled from public life to his books at his beloved Monticello like "a prisoner released from his chains." There he became an indefatigable writer of letters, many of which are minor treatises on a wide variety of subjects.

One abiding purpose runs through the whole of his public career; one pervasive philosophy dominates it: he was a lifelong advocate of liberty for all. He insisted that man should be free, and he was persuaded that, once free, mankind would progress toward happiness and virtue. Behind all of this lay Jefferson's generous faith in the majority of the people. As the historian Richard Hofstadter has said succinctly, the Federalists "feared, above all, power lodged in the majority. Jefferson feared power lodged anywhere else." When the people become inattentive to government, then "you and I," he wrote to Edward Carrington, "and Congress and Assemblies, judges and governors shall all become wolves." Such statements permanently enshrined Thomas Jefferson as the major apostle of individual freedom and the prophet of radical democracy—and set him off so sharply and distinctly in historical memory.

The impressive memorial to Jefferson in Washington, D.C., is tangible evidence of his recognized membership in the trinity of American immortals, along with George Washington and Abraham Lincoln. The supreme eminence of these three presidents remains unchallenged: Washington is the major symbol of the new republic, Lincoln of the preserved Union, and Jefferson of a free and independent new nation. Lincoln himself once said, "The principles of Jefferson are the definitions and axioms of free society." All who are zealous for the maintenance of individual freedom and religious liberty, all who retain faith in reason and human dignity, will rejoice on this Independence Day at the reaffirmation of devotion to the principles to which Thomas Jefferson dedicated his life.

The Magazine ANTIQUES is pleased to add two footnotes to the vast published store of Jeffersoniana this month: one is a fascinating bit of detective work by a young librarian in Hawaii on the lost Giuseppe Ceracchi bust; the other, on the recently discovered wooden model of the classical askos, is by the distinguished editor of *The Papers of Thomas Jefferson* at Princeton University and represents mellow scholarship at its best.

Wendell Garrett

Antiques

In drafting their first state constitutions in the 1770's, the founding fathers succeeded in "building a wall of separation between Church and State," in Jefferson's words; the ratification of the Federal Constitution in 1788 constituted the first bold acceptance of the principle that a man's religion was irrelevant to government by forbidding all religious tests for officeholding. Never before had a national state been prepared to dispense with an official religion as a prop for its authority; never before had the church been set adrift without state support. Yet the perspicacious French traveler and commentator Alexis de Tocqueville was profoundly impressed by the position of the church and the influence of religion in America during the early 1830's: "There is no country in the world," he wrote in his *Democracy in America,* "in which the Christian religion retains a greater influence over the souls of men than in America, and there can be no greater proof of its utility, and its conformity to human nature, than that its influence is most powerfully felt over the most enlightened and free nation on earth." And fifty years later, Lord Bryce, de Tocqueville's worthy successor from England, observed: "Christianity is in fact understood to be, though not the legally established religion, yet the national religion." But the American separation of church and state was not the least bit antireligious: our presidents invoke the Deity and offer prayers; our armies and legislatures maintain chaplains; and our state and federal governments encourage religion through the remission of taxes.

The history of religion in America is curiously baffling in its labyrinthine complexity. The Puritans of Massachusetts Bay lived in a strict theocracy with the conviction that they had made a covenant with an inscrutable god. Governor John Winthrop told them that in this unique moral venture they would be "as a Citty upon a Hill." But very soon "the New England way" began to fray around the edges and well before 1700 the entire fabric was disintegrating. This was the "declension" that Puritan preachers decried from the pulpit in their celebrated jeremiads to dozing congregations. Children of the first-generation saints were not coming forward to claim the essential "converting experience." Out of desperation the magistrates departed from orthodoxy and devised the Halfway Covenant, whereby their less devout children could become church members simply by declaring their belief in Calvinist principles. However, these members were allowed neither to take communion nor vote in parish affairs.

The first New England colonists were proud of the thoroughness with which they discarded Old World corruption. The observance of Christmas, for example, was studiously ignored for the reasons that it was pagan in origin, and also because the day had become the occasion of excessive merrymaking and wild goings on in Elizabethan England. It was not until early in the nineteenth century that Christmas as we know it with plum pudding and carols, a tree and presents, came to be celebrated widely by Americans. The festively decorated open-hearth kitchen on the cover this month with its table laden with the makings for a Christmas feast from the Israel Crane House in Montclair, New Jersey, is a delightful reminder of that bygone era.

For generations after Independence, Americans turned deliberately inward, cultivating their own sectional interests with the same intensity that they cultivated their soil. In the long-settled regions of the South, religion became of even less import as the region barricaded itself in a closed society during the ante-bellum period. On the frontier, however, the first few years of the nineteenth century were marked by a sweeping religious upsurge known as the Great Revival which drew thousands of families to camp meetings where relays of preachers urged them on the road to salvation through sermons morning, noon, and night. Often the effects of the spirit took extravagant physical form: hysteria broke out and the people in the congregation were prone to twitch, jerk, leap, shout, sob, and emit a strange sound called the holy laugh. This second Great Awakening, in the tradition of Jonathan Edwards and George Whitefield sixty years earlier, spread like prairie wildfire across the new regions which lacked permanent churches.

But in New England the country people went on living much as they always had, clustered around a small town whose houses faced on the dignified village green and whose life centered in the meetinghouse. Harriet Beecher Stowe described the workings of a New England church in *Oldtown Folks,* a novel set in one of these towns in the early republic: "High and low, good and bad, refined and illiterate, barbarian and civilized, negro and white, the old meetinghouse united us all on one day of the week, and its solemn services formed an insensible but strong bond of neighborhood charity. . . . The man or woman cannot utterly sink who on every seventh day is obliged to appear in decent apparel, and to join with all the standing and respectability of the community in a united act of worship." The quiet interior scene from the Congregational Church in East Haddam, Connecticut, on the frontispiece seems almost unchanged after nearly two centuries; it is a reminder at this season of the strict, uncompromising religion of our forefathers and its enduring legacy: the sense of guilt, the prudishness, the industry, and the curious combination of materialism and idealism that are regarded by the rest of the world as typically American qualities.

Wendell Garrett

Antiques

THE BICENTENNIAL of the American Revolution will soon be hard upon us, for better or worse. One has good reason to view the prospect of this impending national birthday with a mixture of lofty idealism and severe misgivings: it is evident that any number of hucksters of historical hokum do not intend to allow it to pass without taking full advantage of a gullible public. But there are also signs of the reaffirmation of the dignity of man and the precepts of democracy, liberty, and justice—those principles that Thomas Jefferson called "self-evident"—in a stunning galaxy of exhibitions to be mounted by the complex of museums that makes up the Smithsonian Institution. One of these currently on view at the National Portrait Gallery is devoted to the prologue of the Revolution as seen through the portraits of the leading personalities on both sides of that conflict and related historic artifacts, imprints, and manuscripts (see p. 25). One of the stars of that show is the portrait of Thomas Jefferson at forty-three (frontispiece) when he was serving as America's minister plenipotentiary to the Court of Versailles. It was painted by Mather Brown at his London studio in Cavendish Square when the Massachusetts-born artist was himself only twenty-four. This life portrait of Jefferson, the earliest known, was painted in the spring of 1786 and has a tangled provenance that has been straightened out recently by Alfred L. Bush in *The Life Portraits of Thomas Jefferson* (1962) and Andrew Oliver in *Portraits of John and Abigail Adams* (1967). Brown painted two portraits each of Jefferson and John Adams in London between 1786 and 1788. Of the four portraits two are known today: one of Jefferson owned by a direct descendant of John Adams, and one of Adams in the Boston Athenaeum. By a strange coincidence, both are the replicas the men gave each other during their lifetimes.

The same kind of patient historical scholarship used to sort out the Mather Brown portraits of Adams and Jefferson was practiced by William Nathaniel Banks to attribute a number of American views to the French artist Victor de Grailly and his compatriot Hippolyte Louis Garnier, whose *United States Capitol* appears on the cover. This view up Pennsylvania Avenue in about 1845 cannot have been dramatically different from that seen by Jefferson on the first Wednesday in March 1801 when, attended by friends, he strolled from his lodgings at Conrad and McMunn's to his inauguration in the Senate Chamber as third president of the republic. De Grailly and Garnier's paintings, which followed the engraved landscapes of William Henry Bartlett, can be appreciated more fully for their celebration of the spaciousness and richness of the American scene by French painters who apparently never visited the North American continent.

The stories of the Jefferson portrait and the De Grailly and Garnier landscapes are true history, not the currently fashionable fictionalized biography and pseudo-history which fabricate the past to satisfy the transitory preoccupations of the present. Playing such tricks on the dead is at best gratuitous and at worst grossly misleading. That Gore Vidal's eulogy of the scoundrel Aaron Burr and Fawn M. Brodie's sensational view of Jefferson's morals—in reviving the miscegenation legend and assigning to him the paternity of the children borne by his quadroon slave, Sally Hemings—should have reached the list of best-selling books presents a disturbing picture of the popular American appetite for half-baked and heavily spiced history and biography on the eve of the Bicentennial. This is the more distressing in view of the nearly simultaneous publication of volume nineteen of the magisterial Princeton University edition of *The Papers of Thomas Jefferson,* meticulously edited by Julian P. Boyd, and volume five of the comprehensive biography of *Jefferson and His Times,* written with impressive erudition by Dumas Malone. These monumental works of seasoned scholarship unfortunately reach only a comparatively small reading audience and fail to claim the prime review space seemingly reserved for more sensational biographical revelations. In the current craze to accept at face value Miss Brodie's speculation that Jefferson had commerce with Sally Hemings, Malone's stronger evidence that she was the mistress of Jefferson's nephew Peter Carr, which he published in his fourth volume, goes largely unnoticed.

Early in 1801 when Burr and Jefferson, the two Republican candidates for the presidency, each had the same number of electoral votes, the arch Federalist Alexander Hamilton broke the deadlock declaring: "I have nothing against Aaron Burr except that he is a political demagogue . . . completely unfit for high office. I have nothing in favor of Thomas Jefferson except that he is an honest man. I charge you to make him President of the United States." But the political campaign was costly to Jefferson, whose name and reputation were attacked in the bitterest terms. Still smarting from the slander and epithets, Jefferson wrote his first inaugural address, sounding the keynote of his administration: "We are all republicans—we are federalists." As late as 1826, a few days before he died, Jefferson wrote with the moving honesty characteristic of the many letters which form the record of his life: "The mass of mankind has not been born with saddles on their backs, nor a favored few booted and spurred, ready to ride them legitimately, by the grace of God." And with this last declaration of faith in the principle of equality, he was ready for the last great adventure—"untried by the living, unreported by the dead."

Wendell Garrett

Antiques

I think it of very great importance to fix the taste of our country properly, and I think your examples will go very far in that respect. It is therefore my wish that everything about you should be substantially good and majestically plain, *made to endure.*

—Gouverneur Morris to George Washington, January 1790

EVER SINCE THE Maypole in Merry Mount around 1625—when Thomas Morton and his men sported with the "lasses in beaver coats" and raised a storm of criticism in the Bay Colony for their promiscuity—Americans have been obsessed with virtue. As God's chosen people with a special mission and a classic destiny, the eighteenth century believed that an antithesis existed between the *virtue* of the New World and the *vice* of the Old. The simplicity and innocence of America were to replace the complexity and corruption of Europe. Virtue was more than merely abstract morality or social pietism: it dictated a disinterested concern for the welfare of the body politic; it combined respect for industry with a sense of discipline. It meant more than the avoidance of sin: it was the pragmatic wisdom of a Benjamin Franklin—the spokesman and emblem of those prudential virtues, hard work and thrift, upon which the economic life of the Colonies depended. "In order to secure my Credit and Character as a Tradesman," he wrote in his *Autobiography,* "I took care not only to be in *Reality* Industrious and frugal, but to avoid all *Appearances* of the Contrary." Only in an open society, free of the inhibiting European apparatus of hereditary caste and class, as Franklin understood so well, could the artisan strike out on his own and achieve success. With this emphasis on industriousness and utility, on self-help and materialism, the role of the arts in a democratic society became increasingly ambiguous. The arts, in the words of Benjamin Rush, were known to "flourish chiefly in wealthy and luxurious countries." If Americans were to create a republican style in the arts—a style that was "majestically plain" in Gouverneur Morris' felicitous phrase—they had to avoid the over-refinement and luxury of the arts of Europe.

This theme of European decadence became the motive in the founding fathers' rationale for introducing a republican neoclassicism and a virtuous humanism—a beautiful but fragile ideal—into their own art and literature. When salty John Adams—a secular Puritan at heart—arrived in France he equated the opulence of the buildings, paintings, sculpture, gardens, and furniture with decadence and frivolity, calling them simply "bagatelles, introduced by time and luxury in exchange for the great qualities, and hardy, manly virtues of the human heart." "I cannot help suspecting," he wrote pompously to his wife, "that the more elegance, the less virtue, in all times and countries." He genuinely feared that the American people might become addicted to the luxury-loving, money-mongering idleness which he saw in France and England—cultures perched dangerously near the brink of ruin, eaten away by the disintegrative forces of corruption and vice.

These oracular revolutionaries of the eighteenth century, out of their desire to reconcile virtue and vice, became fascinated with a cyclical theory of history based on Edward Gibbon's *Decline and Fall of the Roman Empire,* the first volume of which appeared in 1776. Gibbon interpreted the life cycle of states like that of human beings: they were born, they matured, and they died in an endless sequence. For the eighteenth century, the history of classical antiquity became "a kind of laboratory in which autopsies of the deceased classical states" were studied with fascination, according to Gordon S. Wood in *The Rising Glory of America, 1760–1820.* "Once the Roman people had become too luxurious, too obsessed with refinements and magnificent living, and too preoccupied with money, their politics had become corrupted, selfishness had dominated, and dissolution had to follow." The lesson of England, sinking under the massive weight of corruption and materialism, was obvious to all. John Adams remarked that "there is never a rising meridian without a setting sun," and Noah Webster noted that all nations "progress from their origins to maturity and decay."

The generation of Americans who lived through the revolutionary era was exultant about the future prospect of America: its innocence, its boundlessness, its goodness, its perfect freedom, its dynamic productivity. The intense provinciality of American culture—its prevailing crudity and rusticity, its lack of sophistication and polish—were now viewed more as advantages rather than as deficiencies. Between the time that the exuberantly carved Philadelphia Chippendale chair was made (cover), derivative of London fashions, and the formally conceived Boston Empire pedestal was constructed (frontispiece), representative of indigenous tastes, Americans moved into another century, not only in time but in thought. This vast transformation in the way they perceived themselves and the world about them—including their furniture—was the real American revolution. Their obsession with virtue growing out of revolutionary republicanism introduced a moral quality into their culture; it helped to shape their furniture into a national style of what might be termed elegant simplicity; or "majestic plainness," as Gouverneur Morris implied; or "ostentatious austerity" as Michael Kammen called it in his recent book *People of Paradox.* It was Alexis de Tocqueville in the 1830's who best delineated these contradictory tendencies in the American arts when he wrote:

> Democratic nations, among whom all these things exist, will therefore cultivate the arts that serve to render life easy in preference to those whose object is to adorn it. They will habitually prefer the useful to the beautiful, and they will require that the beautiful should be useful.

Wendell Garrett

New England is wrote upon my heart in as strong characters as Calais was upon Q. Mary's. . . . I should prefer even my humble cottage upon Milton Hill to the lofty palaces upon Richmond Hill, so that upon the whole I am more of a New England man than ever. . . . I had rather live in obscurity there, than in pomp and splendor here.

—Governor Thomas Hutchinson, August 1774–January 1775

THUS WROTE the ill-fated, former loyalist governor of Massachusetts from the deepening gloom of his exile in England during the American Revolution. Despite all the vilification and abuse he had received at home and despite the cordial reception and honors he was accorded in England (including the award of an honorary doctorate of civil laws by Oxford University on July 4, 1776), his longing to return to America grew stronger with each passing day. Even though he was very much the center of a growing group of American refugees, Hutchinson was increasingly disregarded by the government and became morbidly conscious of what another loyalist refugee, Samuel Curwen, called their "uneasy abode in this country of aliens." His affection for New England was increased with his discontent and misery: he confessed almost sadly, "the passion for my native country returns . . . we live as much in the N. Engd way as ever we can." Homesick for the unobtainable delicacies of Massachusetts, he once wrote an appeal to his son for several bushels of cranberries, and included detailed instructions on how they should be picked and shipped. Like many of his fellow exiles, Hutchinson began to wonder where he might die, rather than live; even here his preference was unshakable: "I had rather die in a little country farm house in N. England than in the best Nobleman's seat in Old England." Of all the loyalists who spent the war years as refugees in England, probably the largest single group was composed of New Englanders who had left when Boston was evacuated by the British. Their spare American habits, their stiff nonconformist provincialism, as well as their lack of money, dimmed the luster of London for many of them who longed for the kind of beautiful, softly rolling landscapes of New England shown elsewhere in this issue.

The American Revolution was more than a revolt against the British Empire—it was a civil war. And the loyalists, the dissenters, were the losers. It was they who dared to criticize or oppose the progress toward armed conflict, who wanted to correct the faults of the imperial system without losing their place in the Empire, who feared the radical and democratic implications of Whig ideology. There were approximately 480,000 loyalists among the 2,500,000 colonists. Of that number, between sixty and eighty thousand became exiles. The seven thousand who went to England hoped to find not only safety but an atmosphere of tolerance and respect they felt they deserved. Instead they suffered a most abject kind of anguish and a most bitter sense of failure: they lost not only their argument, their war, and their place in American society, but later even their proper place in history. No less patriotic and virtuous than those who opposed them, their expulsion remains one of the tragedies of American history. Our failure to understand their dilemma better in the past reflects an alarming uniformity of the American historical imagination and a certain impoverishment of our conservative tradition.

It should be easier now, at a cool distance from the fires of revolution, to see the weaknesses of the Whiggish interpretation of how Americans won their war of independence. Their first answer was at once the most agreeable and the most irrefutable: victory was Providential, for God favored the American cause. Since the nineteenth century, conjectures about American victory have become somewhat more sophisticated. In what might be called a secular version of the Providential explanation, nature and geography are alleged to have fought on the side of the Americans—and indeed they did. How ridiculous, exclaimed Tom Paine, to suppose that a continent should belong to an island! Some historians have argued that Britain lost the war because of incompetence and corruption, of squalid politics and corrupt patronage at home. More recently historians have come to believe that the war with the American colonies burgeoned almost overnight into a global war, fought not merely by a handful of ragged Continentals in the American wilderness but also by a formidable coalition of France, Spain, and the Netherlands. Ironically enough, it was Yorktown—not far from Jamestown, the first permanent English settlement in America—that was decisive; a new world came into being when Lord Cornwallis and his troops marched out to surrender to the words and tune of:

If ponies rode men, and if grass ate the cows,
And cats should be chased into holes by the mouse,
If summer were spring and the other way around,
Then all the world would be upside down.

It was indeed a world turned upside down: the first crack in that noble edifice, and what is now perhaps only a nostalgic dream, of the British Empire. "O, God, it is all over," cried the luckless Lord North when he heard the news of Yorktown. From their former high hopes and eager expectations, the American loyalists in exile slipped into disillusionment and despair—and finally historical oblivion. Even in defeat and anguished silence, they deserve better than they have received.

Wendell Garrett

Antiques

. . . we utterly dissolve & break off all political connection which may have heretofore subsisted between us & the people or parliament of Great Britain; and finally we do assert and declare these colonies to be free and independant states, and that as free & independant states they shall hereafter have power to levy war, conclude peace, contract alliances, establish commerce, & to do all other acts and things which independant states may of right do. And for the support of this declaration we mutually pledge to each other our lives, our fortunes, & our sacred honour.

—Thomas Jefferson, *Declaration of Independence*, original rough draft, 1776

IT IS NOW two centuries since the American people commenced what they very well understood to be an experiment in liberty that assumed a coherent political doctrine of dissent. Men like Jefferson and Franklin and Adams were steeped in the knowledge of history from the classical times to their own day; they were learned in the history of law and constitutional government, and realistic about the defects and dangers of democracy. While they staunchly defended the need for majority rule and essential political liberties in order to create a framework in which all equally could enjoy their "unalienable Rights . . . [to] Life, Liberty and the Pursuit of Happiness," theirs was not the voice of absolute idealism or doctrinaire liberalism. They were sensible men, who regarded every form of government in this treacherous world as problematic and liable to corruption. Confining the popular spirit was essential, they felt, to preserve this brave American experiment in human freedom and the faith that sustained it. The founding fathers feared uncontrolled democracy as much as they did totalitarianism. But they knew that man must choose between competing evils and goods. Their experience and wisdom taught them to preserve the right of dissent.

From the beginning, our history has been rooted in dissent and the willingness of successive generations to make the boldest of gambles. "We hope to plant a nation, where none before hath stood," wrote an early Virginia chronicler. On the successful fulfillment of this hope depended the aspirations of the thirty-five million immigrants who crossed the Atlantic in the century after 1820 to conquer a wilderness and convert it to a civilization. Everything here was new and unique. Never before in recorded history had so spacious and rich a virgin land been thrown open for settlement. Never before had such a luxuriant supply of gifted philosopher-statesmen been presented with a clean slate and commissioned to launch an experiment in self-government.

America was always considered exceptional and that the American cause had opened a new chapter in the history of mankind was reaffirmed by foreign liberal intellectuals throughout the nineteenth century. The French social philosopher Alexis de Tocqueville wrote:

> In that land the great experiment of the attempt to construct society upon a new basis was to be made by civilized man; and it was there, for the first time, that theories hitherto unknown, or deemed impracticable, were to exhibit a spectacle for which the world has not been prepared by the history of the past.

America was not just one more empire but a transforming presence whose emergence at the center of history had been made possible not only by the providential wealth of a virgin continent, but by the first successful application of a new principle in human affairs. In an expansion of Tocqueville's theme of American uniqueness, the German philosopher Hegel, in his *Philosophy of History*, remarked:

> America is therefore the land of the future, where, in the ages that lie before us, the burden of the World's History shall reveal itself. . . . It is a land of desire for all those who are weary of the historical lumber room of old Europe.

Nature itself has imposed on us the necessity of invention and experimentation, and we have always been happiest when we could discover a mechanical solution to the most difficult problems: the cotton gin, the steamboat, the Colt revolver, barbed-wire fencing, the harvester, and a thousand other inventions of a practical character. And what was true in a material sense was true in a philosophical sense. Benjamin Franklin (frontispiece)—self-educated, self-motivated, diligent, inventive, the first citizen of the Colonies, and one of the first of the Western world—wrote to his English friend Jonathan Shipley in 1786:

> You seem desirous of knowing what Progress we make here in improving our Governments. We are, I think, in the right Road of Improvement, for we are making Experiments. I do not oppose all that seem wrong, for the Multitude are more effectually set right by Experience, than kept from going wrong by Reasoning with them.

Today, the belief in American uniqueness has all but vanished in our loss of faith in the nation's future. One of the gravest dangers that confronts us is the temptation to reject the long tradition of experimentation—the tradition of taking bold risks on the intelligence, the fortitude, and the virtue of the American people. What has happened to the American dream as we approach the third American century and the second Western millennium? We want guarantees, security, and certainty, forgetting that certainty is an illusion, and forgetting, too, Oliver Wendell Holmes' admonition that "the constitution is an experiment, as all life is an experiment," and that "every day we have to wager our salvation upon some prophecy based upon imperfect knowledge."

Wendell Garrett

Antiques

With our fate will the destiny of unborn Millions be involved . . . .

—George Washington, *Circular Letter to the States,* 1783

WHEN THE Continental Congress took the thirteen Colonies into war, George Washington was officially established not only as the commander in chief but also as the public symbol in the national Valhalla of the fight for popular sovereignty. While Congress, its membership ever shifting, wallowed in indecision, Washington became the power that held the cause together. His aloofness, his dignity, his reverence for God, his massiveness of character, his sense of destiny were proverbial in the public imagination: he was an abstraction of the aspirations of his countrymen. Following his presidency, he quit the life of power to go back to his farm in the role of Cincinnatus, the virtuous Roman husbandman who left the furrow to take up arms for his country, and, duty fulfilled, returned to the plow—or in this case to his "villa," as Washington called Mount Vernon.

While he was president, Washington was libeled with a venom aimed at few of his successors, and after his death on December 14, 1799, he was accused of every kind of crime, including stealing from the public treasury. Yet by the outbreak of the Civil War he had been elevated to a stature he had never attained in life. He had become the Father of his Country.

Americans' desperate need for a dignified national hero arose from the fact that the nation sprang into being almost before it had time to acquire a history. With astonishing energy and ingenuity Americans set about to provide both the institutions and symbols of nationhood. The institutions—Constitution, Federal government, judicial system, and political parties—they contrived with consummate skill. But what is most impressive is the speed and effectiveness with which they conjured up all of the symbols that go into the making of a nation: a flag, a national anthem, mottoes and myths, legends and traditions, a capital city and a Capitol. The same generation, indeed the same individuals, who figuratively laid the cornerstone of the nation literally laid the cornerstone of the new Capitol. And Washington was both symbol and driving force in both enterprises. The new capital city was to be across the river from Mount Vernon and, what is more, it was to bear his name.

Nothing better reveals the cultic, sacred character of Washington than his portraits. The stereotype was rendered by Gilbert Stuart in his highly idealized, unfinished, but widely copied Athenaeum portrait which is suffused with an otherworldly haze. Emerson, in 1852, after studying for some days the portrait of Washington that hung in his dining room, wrote in his journal of its "Appalachian strength": "The heavy, leaden eyes turn on you, as the eyes of an ox in a pasture. And the mouth has gravity and depth of quiet, as if this MAN had absorbed all the serenity of America, and left none for his restless, rickety, hysterical countrymen." Not oil, but marble seemed the most appropriate material for the artist wishing to do justice to the character of Washington.

Houdon's full-length image of Washington stands in the rotunda of the state capitol in Richmond (cover). When Robert E. Lee appeared before the Virginia convention in April 1861 to take command of the armed forces of that state, he was seen to look up at this statue as he entered the building. The president of the convention compared Lee to that earlier patriot, ready to draw his sword not in aggression but in defense of his native land. It was the later statue by Greenough, modeled after Phidias' colossal Zeus for the temple of Olympia, which showed Washington seated on a carved throne, naked to the waist, with drapery over his legs and sandals on his feet, that stirred the greatest controversy. "Washington was too prudent, and careful of his health," wrote the New York socialite Philip Hone, "to expose himself thus in a climate so uncertain as ours, to say nothing of the indecency of such exposure, a subject on which he was known to be exceedingly fastidious." The public shock at the fleshy version of their hero resulted in the removal of the statue to the decent obscurity of an alcove in the Smithsonian Institution. "Did anybody ever see Washington nude?" Nathaniel Hawthorne asked in 1858. "It is inconceivable. He had no nakedness, but I imagine he was born with his clothes on, and his hair powdered, and made a stately bow on his first appearance in the world." The public's outrage about the half-naked Washington made it easier for the Washington Monument Association to raise funds in the 1830's and 1840's for no human monument however godlike in appearance, but for a geometric obelisk.

Wendell Garrett

Antiques

What spectacle can be more edifying or more seasonable, than ... Liberty & Learning, each leaning on the other for their mutual and surest support?

James Madison to W. T. Barry, August 4, 1822

For Shakespeare, in 1588, the verb "to educate" meant to provide formal instruction from teachers, but its broader definition among colonists in seventeenth-century America involved new attitudes about authority, mobility, merit, and success which have come to characterize American society today. Education established lines of loyalty, obedience, and respect within families and communities. It concerned personal and public morality as well as the relationships between masters and servants and between settlers and Indians.

The responsibility for overseeing familial education and compelling colonial households to be a school of spiritual instruction was vested not in the clergy, as it had been in England, but in the selectmen. As early as 1642 Massachusetts law empowered the selectmen of each town "to take account from time to time of all parents and masters, and of their children, concerning their calling and employment of their children, especially of their ability to read and understand the principles of religion and the capital laws of the country," and authorized them, with the consent of any court or magistrate, to "put forth apprentices the children of such as they shall [find] not to be able and fit to employ and bring them up." Similar statutes were passed in the other colonies as much to affirm the value of learning as to increase the political autonomy and economic self-sufficiency of the Colonies.

By 1702 Cotton Mather exhorted parents to make their sons "beneficial to human society" and reminded them of the "mischief of ignorance" and the social uselessness of the uneducated man. And by 1776, in North Carolina at least, the long agitation for public education bore fruit in the state's constitution, which provided for the establishment of the University of North Carolina (frontispiece).

When Abraham Lincoln (cover) offered himself as a candidate for the General Assembly of Illinois in 1832 at the age of twenty-three (and was defeated), he expressed his concern "that every man may receive at least, a moderate education, and thereby be enabled to read the histories of his own and other countries, by which he may duly appreciate the value of our free institutions. ... "

Scribbling travelers visiting this country between the Revolution and the Civil War commented frequently on the high intelligence of the average American. Basil Hall, who had been told that he would find American farmers to be "intelligent citizens," reported in 1829 that schools succeeded in teaching elementary subjects to large masses of the population, even if these schools did not produce what he considered real education: "In one word, there is abundant capacity, and abundant desire to learn in America, but by no means any adequate reward for learning." On the literacy of the average American and the ingenuity of the Yankee workman, Thomas Cather said, "They possess great intelligence, energy, enterprise, and perseverance, all the elements necessary to make a flourishing commercial people, but they lack the qualities of a noble and generous nation." The intelligence and restlessness of the American workingman—his go-ahead spirit, his desire to improve his fortune quickly through the application of his ingenuity and wits—attracted the attention of innumerable commentators. Michael Chevalier observed that "in Massachusetts and Connecticut, there is not a laborer who has not invented a machine or a tool." The inventive American, he said, was "devoured with a passion for movement," and was "fit for all sorts of work except those which require a careful slowness. Those fill him with horror; it is his idea of hell."

The utilitarianism of the American experience often nullified educational theories, yet Cotton Mather and the Puritan cosmology, Jefferson and the American Enlightenment, and Lincoln and the era of universal reform were alike in their concern for the same core ideas within education. They valued order in society, and order in learning; they respected the ancient ideas of truth, beauty, goodness, and justice; and above all in their infinite hope and infinite discontent they took nothing for granted but the right of inquiry.

Despite major readjustments in our thinking about nature and human nature during the romantic era, many of the central ideas and classic definitions of education remained with us into the present century. They are what remain when we have forgotten everything that we have learned.

Wendell Garrett

Antiques

A "Museum" in the American sense of the word means a place of amusement, wherein there shall be a theatre, some wax figures, a giant and a dwarf or two, a jumble of pictures, and a few live snakes. In order that there may be some excuse for the use of the word, there is in most instances a collection of stuffed birds, a few preserved animals, and a stock of oddly assorted and very dubitable curiosities; but the mainstay of the "Museum" is the "live art," that is, the theatrical performance, the precocious mannikins, or the intellectual dogs and monkeys.

—Edward Peron Hingston, *The Genial Showman, Being Reminiscences of the Life of Artemus Ward,* 1870

THE DEVELOPMENT of the museum as a cultural institution from its incidental emergence in ancient Greece through the proliferation of "cabinets" of natural and artificial curiosities is a long and fascinating story.

Nathaniel Hawthorne poked fun at antiquarians and the museums they assembled in a story entitled "A Virtuoso's Collection," first published in 1842. In this flight of fancy he described a museum (actually the museum of the Salem East India Marine Society, founded in 1799) whose stuffed animals included the wolf that ate Little Red Riding Hood, Cerberus, Dr. Johnson's cat Hodge, Shelley's skylark, and "Coleridge's albatross transfixed with the Ancient Mariner's cross-bow shaft." Among "antiquarian rarities" to be admired were "Charlemagne's sheepskin cloak," "Nero's fiddle," Arthur's sword Excalibur, Peter Stuyvesant's wooden leg, a remnant of the Golden Fleece, the chisel of Phidias, President Jefferson's scarlet breeches, and other objects of curiosity to entertain, enthrall, and frighten patrons. Like many a later museum curator, Hawthorne's thought chiefly of acquiring rare and curious objects until his walls were filled and his purse empty.

Unlike the princely collections created by individual munificent patrons in Europe, the first museums in America were formed by associations organized "for Promoting Useful Knowledge" (as is the case of the American Philosophical Society) and to provide a cultural base in an intensely provincial society cut off from established European institutions. One of the first public museums opened here was Charles Willson Peale's in Philadelphia in 1786. There the painter invited the public to inspect his collection of natural wonders as well as his portraits of the founding fathers. With the flora and fauna of a new continent to be investigated, the pursuit of natural philosophy was an important undertaking for learned societies of the arts and sciences. But even early on, the fine and decorative arts were not left out. The Boston Athenaeum, founded in 1807, began to collect and display art early, and the Wadsworth Atheneum opened its galleries built to display art in 1844. And when James Renwick designed the original Smithsonian building in 1847, space designated as an art gallery existed alongside the displays of whale bones and Indian relics.

In the 1870's there developed a new consciousness of artistic values—an awareness that works of art are not simply collectible curiosities but have an aesthetic existence of their own. This caused works of art to be removed from history and science museums and enshrined in museums of their own. Among these new art museums were the Metropolitan Museum of Art in New York and the Museum of Fine Arts, Boston, both founded in 1870; the Philadelphia Museum of Art, founded in 1876; and the Art Institute of Chicago, founded in 1879. Symbolic of the separation is the juxtaposition of the Metropolitan Museum on one side of Central Park and the American Museum of Natural History and the New-York Historical Society on the other.

To enter an American art museum today is to experience a tremendous sense of confidence in American civilization, and never are such museums more culturally and historically correct than when they display "high" and "popular" art together. This is the case in period-room settings at the Henry Francis du Pont Winterthur Museum, to which this issue is devoted. Winterthur, the premier museum of American decorative arts, stands today as the lengthened shadow of two men, Henry Francis du Pont, its founder and patron, and the late Charles Franklin Montgomery, the visionary initiator of the Winterthur Graduate Program in Early American Culture. For a quarter of a century trustees, successive directors, and staff members have perpetuated and elaborated the exalted view of the American decorative arts held by these two men. It is a thrilling experience to visit Winterthur, where the authority and elegance of the objects on display illuminate and inform our sense of national destiny and purpose. It is with pleasure and pride that ANTIQUES pays a return visit to this immense and noble museum which has given us an exemplary symbol of our democratic culture at its best.

Wendell Garrett

. . . every soldier in our army [has] been intimate with his gun from his infancy.

—Thomas Jefferson to Giovanni Fabbroni, 1778

THE AMERICAN Revolution, a peoples' war for political independence, was an upheaval of profound military significance. It caused Britain, the greatest of the European powers, triumphant on land and sea at the end of the Seven Years' War, to lose the bulk of her North American possessions only twenty years later to an inadequately armed, poorly trained, and badly led rebel militia. How is one to explain the outcome of this war? Britain was defeated, some argue, more by a failure of its military policy than by an American victory. More recently—possibly growing out of our experiences with modern revolutionary warfare in Indochina—debate has focused on the more flexible tactics of the American militia which used ambush, hit-and-run skirmishes, shooting from behind cover, marksmanship, and numerous improvements in the rifle—all borrowed in part from the Indians or developed in fighting against the Indians.

During the seventeenth and eighteenth centuries in Europe a vast body of military literature attempted to standardize methods of fighting and prescribe the boundaries of warfare. Generals preferred to engage an enemy away from towns and villages on large open fields where they could properly arrange their bulky battalions as though they were pawns on a chessboard. A battle in the woods, at night, or in winter was fraught with grave risks and would not have been undertaken. War was not waged to exterminate another people or to change their way of life or political institutions. Its objective was much more limited, and it usually simply furthered imperial, dynastic, or commercial strategy. Officers on opposing sides were professionals drawn from the nobility and the upper classes, for whom the duty of serving their prince in battle remained a relic of the feudal age. An international high-style elegance characterized the military uniforms and the embellishments of the weapons (cover) of this fraternity of professionals. If the sovereign could afford it, he would fill the ranks of his army with mercenary professionals such as the Swiss or the Hessians. Otherwise, the rank and file of European armies tended to be the dregs of society, recruited from the jails and taverns.

In America methods of warfare and the nature of the militia system, like other aspects of the emerging American culture, developed out of and were reinforced by the isolation and provincialism of the American situation. From the earliest times, military considerations were important in the lives of the colonists, who were threatened by hostile Indians as well as by intermittent invasions by the French, the Dutch, or the Spanish. As the charter of Massachusetts Bay Colony made clear, the settlers were expected "to incounter, expulse, repell and resist by force of armes, as well by sea as by lands" any attempt to invade or destroy their community. No person was immune from a military obligation in times of crisis, warned the Reverend Ebenezer Gay in 1738: "no Exemption for Men, nor Women; for the Righteous, nor the Wicked; for the High, nor the Low; for the Rich, nor the Poor; for the Strong, nor the Weak; for the Old, nor the Young; for the most buisy; the new-married, nor the faint-hearted."

Boys' pastimes early prepared them for defense. From infancy they were as familiar with the gun as they were with the ax. Writing of life in the Valley of Virginia in the 1760's, Joseph Doddrige noted, "A well grown boy at the age of twelve or thirteen years, was furnished with a small rifle and shot-pouch. He then became a fort soldier, and his port-hole assigned to him. Hunting squirrels, turkeys and raccoons, soon made him expert in the use of his gun." Numerous improvements in the Alpine prototype of the Pennsylvania rifle, later to achieve fame as the Kentucky rifle, resulted in a weapon of unprecedented convenience, economy, and accuracy. The guns and powder horns (see pp. 312-331) of an armed citizenry reflect graphically the differences between methods of warfare in America and Europe.

The American militia system has often been treated as a military joke. George Washington never ceased complaining about his militia—its lack of dependability and discipline, and its cowardice under fire. But the British and their allies were fascinated by the rebel militia, and came to understand better than did many Americans that its part-time soldiers were the sand in the gears of the mighty British war machine. Regular American army units were too few and the theater of war too vast to avoid a heavy reliance upon the militia. By its very nature, the militia system reinforced the provincialism that was a salient characteristic of the colonial period, and it offers some broad insight into American life. The county court, the town meeting, the Congregational church organization, and the military unit consisted of local people under local leadership meeting local needs. During the Revolution the militia enforced law, maintained order, and nullified every British effort to impose royal authority. It regularly made the British light infantry, the German Jägers, and Tory raiders pay a high price for their constant marauding, and it never failed in a real emergency to provide reinforcements for state and Continental regular forces. Indeed, the militia system became so entrenched in American life that the second amendment to the Federal Constitution provided: "A well regulated Militia being necessary to the security of a free State, the right of the people to keep and bear Arms, shall not be infringed."

From the British viewpoint, the militia was a virtually inexhaustible reservoir of rebel military power. Like a great spongy mass without a vital center, it could be temporarily maimed but not destroyed. Its tactics unnerved the rigidly trained professional army, and in the end helped to convince British officers that subduing the American populace was a hopeless task.

Wendell Garrett

Under the spreading chestnut tree
the village smithy stands;
The smith a mighty man is he
With large and sinewy hands.
And the muscles of his brawny arms
Are strong as iron bands.

Henry Wadsworth Longfellow, "The Village Blacksmith," 1841

Antiques

THE SMALL-TOWN blacksmith—that Jack-of-all-trades laboring alone at his forge and anvil—has been widely celebrated in poetry and painting as the personification of rugged individualism and the work ethic. As Longfellow's poem continues, "His brow is wet with honest sweat,/ He earns whate'er he can,/ And looks the whole world in the face,/ For he owes not any man." He has been idealized as a representative of the independent yeoman mechanic engaged in "Arts wherein the Hand and Body are more concerned than the Mind"; he has been viewed as the tragic victim of the painful transition to factory life and machine labor, his fixed work patterns and dream of success threatened and eventually destroyed under the showering sparks and acrid smoke of modern technology. In reconstructing the everyday texture of this traditional working-class world with the help of artisan's tools (cover) and products (frontispiece), we have too easily assumed that the Protestant work ethic was deeply ingrained and widely shared in the American experience. In fact, the impressive work of recent labor historians has indicated that in this premodern world of craftsmen American work patterns tended to be highly irregular and undisciplined and that even with industrialization these working people clung stubbornly to their chaotic habits.

One New Hampshire textile factory, for example, forbade "spirituous liquor, smoking, nor any kind of amusement . . . in the workshops, yards, or factories" and promised the "immediate and disgraceful dismissal" of employees found gambling, drinking, or committing "any other debaucheries." Absenteeism was frequent among the Pennsylvania ironworkers at the rural Hopewell Village Forge; hunting, harvesting, wedding parties, frequent "frolicking" that sometimes lasted for days, and uproarious Election and Independence Day celebrations plagued cost-conscious manufacturers and mill operators. When Alexander Hamilton proposed his grand scheme to industrialize the young republic, an intimate commented, "Unless God should send us saints for workmen and angels to conduct them, there is the greatest reason to fear for the success of the plan." Benjamin Franklin shared such fears and lamented the absence of regular work habits among his contemporaries: "Saint *Monday*," he said in 1768, "is as duly kept by our working people as *Sunday*; the only difference is that instead of employing their time cheaply at church they are wasting it expensively at the ale house." Franklin believed that if poor houses shut down, "Saint Monday and Saint Tuesday" would "soon cease to be holidays."

The sparsity of population in early America resulted in a labor shortage that contributed in part to these spasmodic work habits. As early as 1639 one New Englander observed that if existing wages were maintained, "the servants will be masters and the masters servants." In his *Inquiry into the Nature and Causes of the Wealth of Nations*, published in 1776, Adam Smith noted that wages were much higher in North America than in any part of England. Observing rising wages and declining standards in America, Michel Guillaume Jean de Crèvecoeur complained, "Our mechanics and tradesmen are very dear and sometimes great bunglers." To keep wages down, manufacturers often employed Negro slaves. In the 1730's New York mechanics and artisans protested the "pernicious practice of breeding slaves to trade," forcing free workers to seek employment in other colonies. Another competitor was the half-time farmer who came to town during winter and returned to the farm in time for the spring planting. One New York mechanic wrote in 1757, "A Farmer ought to employ himself in his proper occupation without meddling with Smiths, Masons, Carpenters, Coopers, or any other mechanical Arts, except making and mending his Plow, Harrow, or any other utensil for farming." Without binding apprenticeship rules journeymen frequently moved haphazardly from craft to craft. In New Jersey the complaint was made that "Tradesmen . . . are permitted to follow their Occupations, having served a Master-Workman not above two or three Years, and sometimes not above a few months . . . ; by which the country is imposed on, having their work done by the Halves."

Such erratic behavior and stubborn attitudes among early American artisans and craftsmen reveal an entirely different work ethic than the one we traditionally attribute to our ancestors.

Wendell Garrett

Were we required to characterise this age of ours by any single epithet, we should be tempted to call it, not an Heroical, Devotional, Philosophical, or Moral Age, but, above all others, the Mechanical Age. It is the Age of Machinery, in every outward and inward sense of that word.

Thomas Carlyle, "Signs of the Times," *Edinburgh Review*, 1829

By 1829, when Carlyle's essay on machinery appeared and was read in America, machine power had begun to play an important part in American life. In that year Jacob Bigelow, a Harvard professor, coined the word "technology" to describe this agent of change for a totally new way of life. By then a profitable factory system was already firmly established in New England and the machine had created entirely new landscapes: slag heaps, red-brick factories, and congested mill towns filled with houses for the workers; even the countryside was transformed by new macadam roads, canals, viaducts, and embankments. But it was above all the steam locomotive that became a kind of national obsession—the "industrial revolution incarnate," as one historian called it.

Earlier machines had aroused no such general enthusiasm: for all their usefulness, Oliver Evans' automated flour mill, John Fitch's paddle-propelled steamboat, Eli Whitney's cotton gin, and the mass-produced firearm with interchangeable parts appeared at the time to be simply improvements on labor-saving devices. But the locomotive—the iron horse or fire Titan—became simultaneously an American symbol of progress and a philosophical image. As John Stuart Mill argued in his brilliant review of Alexis de Tocqueville's *Democracy in America* in 1840, to see a locomotive in the American landscape is to know the superiority of the present over the past: "The mere visible fruits of scientific progress in a wealthy society, the mechanical improvements, the steam-engines, the railroads, carry the feeling of admiration for modern and disrespect for ancient times, down even to the wholly uneducated classes." By the outbreak of the Civil War thirty-one thousand miles of railroad were in operation, and by 1869 the first transcontinental line was completed. The reality of progress was obvious to everyone.

On the other hand, as Carlyle wrote, there is an "inward sense" to the word machinery. The very qualities that make for the success of a machine—its power, precision, and tireless ability to repeat the same action—were debilitating to the worker, making his labors meaningless by their mechanistic nature.

The new dangers and the new heroism of the machine age profoundly influenced every aspect of the Victorian mind and culture, including the mechanical production of furniture (frontispiece). This ambivalent attitude toward the machine engendered contrasting modes of viewing technology and raised disturbing questions. How could this nation continue to define its purpose as the pursuit of the pastoral ideal while devoting itself relentlessly to production, wealth, and power? It remained for our most serious nineteenth-century thinkers and writers to struggle with these contradictions. In a burst of romantic pastoralism, for example, Emerson wrote, "Things are in the saddle,/And ride mankind." Others, such as Carlyle, H. G. Wells, and Rudyard Kipling, sought to celebrate the machine by making a doctrine of the work ethic—in itself a set of values derived from the machine. This interrelation between the "outward and inward sense" in responding to the machine, these two antithetical ways of treating technology, reflected the ambivalent attitude of nineteenth-century America. The proper metaphor for culture, as Lionel Trilling has suggested in *The Liberal Imagination*, is tension—the attempt to hold together contradictory ideas. And in confronting technology, particularly in aesthetic theory and the production of household furnishings, the Victorians certainly managed to establish a tension between contradictory ideas.

Wendell Garrett

I would rather be right than be President.

Henry Clay, speech in the Senate, 1850

OF THE TWO great rebellions that divide American history into major periods, the second—the one that failed—continues to exert a strong fascination upon the American imagination. Appropriately, even if perfunctorily, we celebrate our nation's birthday and the success of the Revolution on the Fourth of July each year with what might be called an aspirational reaffirmation of the coherent political doctrine, inspired brevity, and solemn cadence of Jefferson's immortal Declaration of Independence. This was a war fought with a foreign adversary to redress fully articulated wrongs, to institute "self-evident" truths, and to lay claim to "unalienable rights." The second bloody conflict, this one between two sections of the same nation, divided cousins and even brothers. More than the Revolution the Civil War in retrospect seems much larger than life. It has the elements of what one writer has called the "American Iliad": the swift movement and fierce struggle of massed armies, the conflict of two civilizations bound together like twin enemies in a trap of their own making, the picturesqueness of a plantation economy doomed by impersonal economics, the awesome magnitude of a million casualties among innocent men exercising the will of their ancestors.

In the preliminary period of mounting debate over slavery, a triumvirate of orators emerged as the greatest political manipulators of America's silver age. Each represented the economic interests of his own region: Henry Clay, the West (see cover); Daniel Webster, the North; and John C. Calhoun, the South. To understand the final crisis of disunion and civil war, the debate prior to 1861 over American slavery and over the nature of the Union and the Constitution becomes of prime significance, as it moved from political to economic and then to moral terms as positions hardened and language flamed. Following the victorious war with Mexico (1846-1848) severe tensions were created in American politics on the question of the extension of slavery into the new territories held by the states in common. When California sought statehood, the stage was set for the great Congressional debate of 1850. For months fulgurous rhetoric and stentorian declamation filled the Senate chamber, and these three old men with their craggy brows, graveyard coughs, and baleful stares became the central figures of the drama.

In early 1850 Henry Clay—the Mill-Boy of the Slashes, the popular Harry of the West, the despised Judas of the West, author of the American system, the Great Pacificator, and three times an unsuccessful candidate for the presidency—rose in the Senate to deliver the greatest speech of his long career. Clay had entered politics in 1798 at the age of twenty-two with a ringing denunciation of the Alien and Sedition Acts; now old and ill and very tired at seventy-three, he was making a last great effort to save his beloved Union. "I hold in my hand," Clay began, "a series of resolutions which I desire to submit to the consideration of this body. Taken together, in combination, they propose an amicable arrangement of all questions in controversy between the free and slave states, growing out of the subject of Slavery." Kindness, forbearance, and concessions would still enable the sections of the country to live together in happiness and peace; disunion would solve no problems. "Conjure . . . at the edge of the precipice," he begged both North and South, "before the fearful and disastrous leap is taken in the yawning abyss below. . . . I implore, as the best blessing which Heaven can bestow upon me upon earth, that if the direful and sad event of the dissolution of the Union shall happen, I may not survive to behold the sad and heart-rending spectacle." Clay strove mightily with all his eloquence, all his extraordinary power of persuasion, all his charm, all his political skill, and all his vast experience to put through his resolutions of compromise. But nobody liked them and he was denounced bitterly from the floor. It was treason: he, a Southern man, a slaveholder, was making concessions to the enemies of slavery and the foes of the South. The old man flung back the taunt. "Sir," he thundered, "I have heard something said about allegiance to the South. I know no South, no North, no East, no West, to which I owe any allegiance."

The country was waiting to hear from the other two members of the triumvirate. On March 4 the desperately ill Calhoun, "Swathed in flannels," sat expressionless as his speech, which was surprisingly free of vituperation and bitterness, was read for him by another senator; by the end of the month he was dead. On March 7 Webster spoke and said, in effect, that since it had plainly come to a choice between abolition and union, he chose the Union; his speech was greeted with a hellish clamor of hisses, jeers, and objurgations, and was climaxed with a shrill catcall from John Greenleaf Whittier, that singularly bloodthirsty Quaker. None of the old men lived to witness the holocaust to come; by their combined efforts they had blocked the way of the Four Horsemen and gave their country peace for ten more years. Clay died on June 29, 1852, and Webster, on October 24 of the same year. Upon Clay's monument is the inscription *No South, no North, no East, no West.*

Wendell Garrett

Antiques

The Plow-man that raiseth Grain is more serviceable to Mankind, than the Painter who draws only to please the Eye. The Carpenter who builds a good House to defend us from the Wind and Weather, is more serviceable than the curious Carver, who employs his Art to please the Fancy.

An Addition to the Present Melancholy Circumstances of the Province Considered, Boston, 1719

THERE HAS ALWAYS been a general feeling that if Washington, D.C., is the political capital and New York City the financial capital, then Boston is the cultural capital of the United States. Yet foreign travelers and native commentators have found the "Athens of America" to be everything from sublime to ridiculous, from a melting pot of democracy to an autocracy ruled by a Brahman caste, from a living force to a city of the dead.

Emerson, for instance, venerated Boston as a "seat of humanity, of men of principle, obeying a sentiment and marching loyally whither that should lead them. . . . the town which was appointed in the destiny of nations to lead the civilization of North America." As recently as 1942 Alfred North Whitehead—a British philosopher of international reputation drawn to Boston in retirement by its galaxy of institutions—observed: "In so far as the world of learning today possesses a capital city, Boston with its various neighboring institutions approximates to the position that Paris occupied in the Middle Ages."

On the other hand, the acerbic Charles Francis Adams complained about the "Hub of the Universe" from his house on the South Shore: "In the course of my life I have tried Boston socially on all sides: I have summered it and wintered it, tried it drunk and tried it sober; and drunk and sober there's nothing in it save Boston. . . . This is the trouble with Boston—it is provincial." It was, as William Dean Howells wrote in *The Rise of Silas Lapham* in 1884, "a society where Middlesexes have married Essexes and produced Suffolks for two hundred and fifty years." H. G. Wells at the beginning of this century depicted Boston culture as tired, archaic, and overrefined: "there broods over the real Boston an immense effect of finality. One feels in Boston, as one feels in no other part of the States, that the intellectual movement has ceased."

Boston's Augustan age was the middle of the nineteenth century, when Emerson, Thoreau, Longfellow, Lowell, Whittier, Hawthorne, Holmes, Prescott, and Parkman were writing books that became American classics. Mens' minds seethed with short cuts to heaven on earth. Lovers of perfection given to improving themselves as well as others, they felt impelled to free slaves, reform drunkards, observe the Sabbath, improve prisons, abolish prostitution, and spread literacy.

The city was a solvent and comfortable place where the descendants of the "codfish aristocracy" (Van Wyck Brooks' evocative phrase) felt it their duty to use the proceeds of commerce and industry to foster intellectual and cultural institutions. Carl Bridenbaugh has labeled this New England attitude one of "practical idealism," growing out of the dichotomy between Puritan idealism and Yankee practicality.

E. L. Godkin, editor of the *Nation*, observed in 1871 that "Boston is the one place in America where wealth and knowledge of how to use it are apt to coincide." The China Trade merchants James and Thomas Handasyd Perkins greatly aided the library of the Boston Athenaeum in the early decades of the nineteenth century. When John Lowell, the son of the textile pioneer on the Merrimack, died prematurely in 1836, he endowed the Lowell Institute, which has ever since provided free public lectures for the citizens of Boston. Forty-five years later the creation of the Boston Symphony Orchestra was the individual inspiration of Major Henry Lee Higginson, an investment banker. Peter Bent Brigham amassed a fortune in Boston real-estate speculation and left it to found the hospital that bears his name. Other instances of Bostonians' enlightened use of prosperity are the creation of the Massachusetts Historical Society, the Boston Public Library, the Massachusetts Institute of Technology, the New England Conservatory of Music, the Boston Medical Library, Radcliffe and Wellesley colleges, and the Museum of Fine Arts.

The museum was founded in 1870 and exactly a century later, inaugurated a department of American decorative arts and sculpture. A sampling of the remarkable objects accessioned by that department during the past decade is the subject of this issue.

Wendell Garrett

Ours is a country, where men start from an humble origin . . . and where they can attain to the most elevated positions, or acquire a large amount of wealth, according to the pursuits they elect for themselves. No exclusive privileges of birth, no entailment of estates, no civil or political disqualifications, stand in their path; but one has as good a chance as another, according to his talents, prudence, and personal exertions. This is a country of self-made men, than which nothing better could be said of any state of society.

[Calvin Colton], *Junius Tracts*, 1844

IT HAS BECOME a fashionable cliché among Americans, immersed as we are in what has been labeled an "Age of Anxiety," to refer to the mid-nineteenth century as the "Golden Age of Homespun," or the "Age of Innovation." Between the War of 1812 and the Civil War, Americans—protected by the great oceans and the absence of formal European alliances—were free to turn their attention to the interior: to grow and develop and expand across the great empty continent. To these men emergent America represented an exciting experiment—a cosmic opportunity to spread the ideals of republicanism, Christianity, and technology across the world horizon.

The Jacksonian age witnessed the so-called rise of the common man: there was an upsurge of admiration and respect for the rude majority who seized control of the government by electing the hero of the battle of New Orleans to the presidency; a democratic spirit emerged that repudiated traditional notions of deference and position. It was a romantic era which affirmed the rights of all men and was strongly influenced by the Revolution that had preceded it. The restless yearning for territorial expansion encompassed the struggle for Texas and Oregon and the window on the Pacific, the war with Mexico, the postwar adventures and skirmishes in the Caribbean, the penetration of South America and the Far East, the competition for Antarctica and the South Sea islands, and the drawing of the great Pacific border at Hawaii.

The same romantic vision of the world inspired Frederic Church to paint his vast canvases of the heart of the Andes and William Sidney Mount to capture the everyday life of Americans in his genre scenes (cover). Mount sought to render with his brush the egalitarian tenets of Jacksonian democracy, and his adherence to these principles shows in his often quoted remark, "Paint pictures that will take with the public—never paint for the few, but the many."

During the half century before the Civil War the self-conscious and self-confident nation teemed with optimism and pride. The country slowly freed itself from its economic dependence on Europe and as a viable domestic economy emerged, the standard of living rose sharply. The generation of painters born after the Revolution was out of touch with the rigid artistic theories of the European academies: some painted meticulous yet lyrical portraits of the beauty and grandeur of the American landscape; others rendered with clarity the workaday lives, humorous foibles, and rude, democratic manners of the uncouth Americans at work, at rest, and at play. Such was this age of hope and promise—a fantastic period of experiment and ferment that changed the tone and style of American society. By mid-century America had proved that the finer fruits of civilization could be democratized without being vulgarized.

This bright vision for American art was shattered and the accepted belief in the perfection of American life was shaken by the sectional controversies and regional rivalries that climaxed in the Civil War. The vulgarity and overtly humorous aspects of traditional genre painting began to lose their appeal to an art audience that was turning toward Victorian morality and idealism; the times dictated that art must edify and uplift. The postwar generation was geared to other values and yearned for sophistication from abroad.

Wendell Garrett

There is, probably, no people on earth with whom business constitutes pleasure, and industry amusement, in an equal degree with the inhabitants of the United States of America. . . . Business is the very soul of an American: he pursues it, not as a means of procuring for himself and his family the necessary comforts of life, but as the fountain of all human felicity . . . it is as if all America were but one gigantic workshop, over the entrance of which there is the blazing inscription, "No admission here, except on business."

Francis J. Grund, *The Americans in Their Moral, Social, and Political Relations,* 1837

SINCE THE eighteenth century one revolution after another—political, religious, or social—has upset the prevailing order, but none has wrought more profound changes than the industrial revolution. In some parts of the Western world, it effaced class distinctions and homogenized the differences in the standard of living, while in some underdeveloped nations its impact has been tragically divisive, encouraging rising expectations that could never be fulfilled. During the half century before 1860 a remarkable generation of inventor-entrepreneurs—the pioneers of American industrial enterprise—disrupted the traditional order and instigated a revolutionary system of manufacture based on interchangeable parts. Close on the heels of the first American Revolution followed a second revolution, heralded not by the thunder of cannon and the rattle of musketry but by the whir of factory machinery and the clang of locomotive bells.

Why did these Americans, who had only recently knit together remote settlements on the fringes of a continental wilderness, change a relatively static, traditional society into a dynamic society built on indigenous innovations in industry, commerce, and agriculture? How does one account for the mechanical genius of an Alfred Hobbs who could turn out locks, or a Samuel Colt who could turn out revolvers, or a Cyrus McCormick who could turn out reapers in such incredible numbers and with such efficiency as to leave the Britons attending the Crystal Palace Exhibition of 1851 dumfounded?

In the past, a number of material reasons have been put forth by historians for these remarkable advances: the absence in the New World of a restrictive feudal past; geographical isolation from the continent of Europe, which was repeatedly devastated by wars; a fertile, well watered agricultural land; abundant wood in the Northeast for the charcoal smelting of widespread ore deposits and scores of streams to produce cheap power.

More recently, scholars have sought cultural clues for industrialization. The ease of incorporating an enterprise and the legal protection of contracts were powerful stimulants to investment, just as the American acceptance of novelty stimulated manufacture. In this fragmented society associations of master craftsmen or guilds were never able to exercise exclusive control over journeymen and apprentices. Exceptionally flexible workbench artisans and craftsmen who had to be Jacks-of-all-trades may have been short on book learning or skilled craftsmanship but they could build effective labor-saving machines. Consequently, many artisans moved readily from making furniture to erecting milling machinery, or from building barns to constructing textile mills, or from working for wages to becoming entrepreneurs. By 1850 the author of a primer for German immigrants could refer without exaggeration to the ability of this one-time colonial land "to compete with the manufacture of even the greatest and oldest industrial countries of the world."

After the War of 1812 migrants poured over the Appalachian Mountains into the fertile farm land of the Northwest Territory and began to produce a surplus of heavy staples—grain, whiskey, lumber, and livestock. Walled off by a barrier of mountains, the region was not easily accessible to manufactured goods from Europe and the Northeast because of the high cost of wagon transport. In a daring act of imagination, planning, and execution some resourceful New Yorkers breached the mountains in 1825 with the Erie Canal and opened the Northwest to commerce and industry. With the growth of internal markets a host of cities and factories sprang into existence—for example, the ceramics manufactories in and around East Liverpool, Ohio (frontispiece). These ventures might be expensive, difficult, even risky, but, fortunately, here was a civilization in which natural resources were superabundant and legal restraints were loose enough to allow bungling innovators to write off mistakes and try again. Out of admiration, envy, and commercial competitiveness men felt free to take a chance, to risk a fortune, to take part in technological change and progress. For good or ill, they shared Andrew Jackson's winged prophecy that America was "manifestly called by the Almighty to a destiny which Greece and Rome, in the days of their pride, might have envied."

Wendell Garrett

By Hammer & Hand, all Arts do stand.

Membership certificate of the New York Mechanick Society, 1791

AT THIS HOLIDAY season—a time for sober thought and quiet reflection—we celebrate colonial craftsmen, those men engaged in the mechanic arts, which were defined by contemporary Englishmen as "such Arts wherein the Hand and Body are more concerned than the Mind." It is the product of their "Hammer & Hand" we display throughout the year on the pages of this magazine; to understand the makers better is to appreciate the artifacts they wrought more fully.

In eighteenth-century England, "mechanic" (the most common and inclusive name for skilled wage-earners and tradesmen) was a pejorative. Samuel Johnson's noted dictionary describes mechanic as "mean, servile; of mean occupation," and the *Oxford English Dictionary* offers an obsolete definition of the word as meaning "belonging to or characteristic of the 'lower orders'; vulgar, low, base." Even in colonial America where men were born free, gentlemen viewed craftsmen with some contempt. In 1744 in New Jersey, Dr. Alexander Hamilton was told by Dr. Thomas Cadwalader that "the House of Assembly here . . . was chiefly composed of mechanicks and ignorant wretches; obstinate to the last degree." As late as 1814 John Lambert, an English traveler, observed: "Those who expect to see a *pure republican equality* existing will find themselves greatly deceived." To the local gentry—particularly merchants, lawyers, and landowners—artisans were neither worthy nor capable of political leadership, nor of full participation in the social life of the community; rather, they were expected to accede to the wisdom and guidance of the wealthier, better educated, and better bred.

Yet, in colonial America the availability of land and a labor intensive economy gave artisans greater wealth; while freedom from guild restraints and apprenticeship restrictions, a comparatively mobile society, and the greater dignity of labor guaranteed the craftsman a better social position than he had ever enjoyed in England. As Carl Bridenbaugh has noted of colonial urban craftsmen, their most singular trait was "their driving desire to get ahead in the world. They were men of ambition; they were consciously on the make. To raise themselves and their families above their present level . . . was their goal." Having helped gain their country's independence by serving in the Continental Army, artisans in the Jeffersonian era strived for ever greater self-respect.

An infectious enthusiasm for mechanization and invention was incorporated into America's dreams of national destiny by the time the revolutionaries launched their experiment in independence. Musing about America's growth in technology, Benjamin Franklin declared that men who invent "new Trades, Arts or Manufactures, or new Improvements in Husbandry, may be properly called Fathers of their Nation." Nathaniel Ames grew exultant with the promise of American improvement:

> Huge Mountains of Iron Ore are already discovered; and vast Stores are reserved for future Generations: This Metal, more useful than Gold or Silver, will employ millions of hands, not only to form the martial Sword and peaceful Share alternately; but an Infinity of Utensils improved in the exercise of Art, and Handicraft amongst Men.

During the Constitutional Convention of 1787, Gouverneur Morris prophesied that the time was not far distant "when this country will abound with mechanics and manufacturers." And indeed, acute foreign observers noticed the adaptive and inventive Americans' familiarity with machines. In 1833 the French visitor Michael Chevalier observed that the American "is a mechanic by nature," while Robert Fulton wrote eloquently of the mechanic who "should sit down among levers, screws, wedges, wheels, etc. like a poet among the letters of the alphabet, considering them as the exhibition of his thoughts, in which a new arrangement transmits a new Idea to the world."

How was it that the craftsman and his spatial mode of thinking flourished especially in the United States in its early decades? Why did a country less culturally developed and less wealthy than the nations of Western Europe assume leadership in certain lines of invention and innovation? It may be that from the beginning those who came to America were conscious of the vast riches and unexampled opportunity offered by an undeveloped continent where so much was to be done. The abundant life that the founding fathers saw ahead required new methods and new institutions. Most evident for the American craftsman was a new life to be won—not an old one to be defended.

Wendell Garrett

Antiques

... tho' the moderns have not made many additions to the art of building, with respect to mere beauty or ornament, yet it must be confess'd, they have carried simplicity, convenience, and neatness of workmanship, to a very great degree of perfection, particularly in England; where plain good sense hath preferr'd these more necessary parts of beauty, which everybody can understand, to that richness of taste which is so much to be seen in other countries, and so often substituted in their room.

William Hogarth, *The Analysis of Beauty*, 1753

The Georgian century was a watershed between England's past and present. The market economy expanded and accelerated, creating an effervescent atmosphere in which individuals could try their fortune and prosper. Between 1721 and 1771 the population increased from 5,300,000 to 6,400,000, English exports doubled in value, and agricultural and industrial production rose by 60 percent. England had only about a third the population of France, her great rival, but in the scale and diversity of her economic activity she supplanted the ambitious, money-making Dutch as the commercial leader of Europe. "There was never from the earliest ages," remarked Dr. Johnson, "a time in which trade so much engaged the attention of mankind, or commercial gain was sought with such general emulation."

Georgian England was a golden age of good design and superlative craftsmanship governed by rules of taste that were deduced from classical antiquity and its revival during the Renaissance. "The sense of sight was honoured as it had not been honoured since the age of Pericles," John Gloag has observed, "and whatever other senses were neglected—such as the sense of smell—the eye was seldom offended."

Universal rules of proportion were observed in building and the making of every conceivable article from a gold snuffbox to an earthenware coffeepot. "Strength with Politeness, Ornament with Simplicity, Beauty with Majesty" were the merits claimed by Colen Campbell for Inigo Jones's Banqueting House in Whitehall, London, and those were the merits to which Georgian writers of elevated prose aspired.

From the 1730's, and the introduction of the rococo, irregularity and asymmetry combined with elegance and lightness were considered the essence of beauty. It was William Hogarth who devised a rationale for the rococo in his *Analysis of Beauty* when he wrote that the straight line was "unnatural" and that a beautiful design should have a serpentine line which curled in all three dimensions to give the outline a novel variety as well as to express motion. He also stressed the fact that nature could provide the entire range of ornament that was needed by the artist or designer. Outdoors this meant that the formal garden of earlier times was swept aside and the landscape park with its trees, plantings, serpentine rivers, and lakes, was brought right up to the house. Parks such as the one at Stourhead House in Wiltshire (cover), were viewed as Arcadia, and the architects in Lord Burlington's circle improved their picturesque quality by ornamenting them with temples, seats, gazebos, grottoes, and sculpture, and everywhere with serpentine paths. In the garden at Stourhead, as in a number of others, romantic sham temples and authentic medieval relics were taking root in the afterglow of the Virgilian landscape at the very moment the landed society of Georgians stood on the threshold of the nineteenth century.

Wendell Garrett

When I think of these times, and call back to my mind the grandeur and beauty of those almost uninhabited shores; . . . when I reflect that all this grand portion of our Union, instead of being in a state of nature, is now more or less covered with villages, farms, and towns, where the din of hammers and machinery is constantly heard; . . . when I see the surplus population of Europe coming to assist in the destruction of the forest, and transplanting civilization into its darkest recesses;—when I remember that these extraordinary changes have taken place in the short period of twenty years, I pause, wonder, and, although I know all to be fact, can scarcely believe its reality.

John James Audubon, *Ornithological Biography*, 1831–1839

Antiques

DURING THE FIRST two generations of the American Republic, interest in science grew into a national concern. Scientific accomplishment was considered a necessary measure of national justification; it became imperative, as a speaker addressing the American Philosophical Society noted in 1785, to demonstrate to the world the "favourable influence that Freedom has upon the growth of useful Sciences and Arts." The Baconian assertion of the utility of science was widely accepted and readily approved in America. Since the main purpose of scientific investigation was practicality, American scientists placed their primary effort in discovering, exploring, charting, collecting, describing, and classifying the natural resources of the virgin continent. The study and description of the thousands of previously unknown species that abounded in America provided artistic naturalists with the irresistible opportunity to draw, paint, or otherwise represent the exotic novelties of America. This was most beautifully true of John James Audubon, whose stunning elephantine edition of *Birds of America* was published over a ten-year period beginning in 1827.

In his lone prowling through the unmapped backwoods and across the prairies of the Ohio and Mississippi valleys—"My knapsack, my gun, and my dog, were all I had for baggage and company," he reported—this self-taught artist and gifted ornithologist frequently referred to himself as a "stranger" in the abundant, untouched landscape. What resulted from those travels were not only the famous illustrations of birds and small mammals but, equally important, the written record of a solitary pioneer in "the dark recesses of the woods" who felt himself a marauder inevitably disrupting the virgin land, violating his intimacy with nature even as he sought to preserve it. What Audubon experienced was a disturbing ambivalence in the face of nature's bounty. He was plagued with the attempt to reconcile the conflicting impulses that motivate the frontier woodsman, "felling and squaring the giant trees," and the frontier naturalist, killing his beloved birds in order to capture them for posterity in pen and ink. Clearly distressed, Audubon revealed the difficulty of maintaining the precarious balance between intimacy and exploitation: settlement would force "commerce to take root," and "transplanting" civilization to the frontier meant it would be impossible to preserve "the country as it once existed, and . . . as it ought to be, immortal." Unable to resolve what is still a central concern with the American psyche—the sense of guilt aroused by the conflict between the pastoral longing to view nature as bountiful and the impulse to dominate and possess the landscape—Audubon attempted to stop time altogether, and preserve the static continuity of a soaring bird and an untamed landscape "before population had greatly advanced." By mid-century the continent had in fact been crossed and the frontier had reached the Pacific. It is both sad and ironic that by the time of Audubon's death in 1851 there were no more virgin landscapes left upon which to project the literary and pictorial image of America as Eden, the idyllic garden of innocence and material ease.

Wendell Garrett

Antiques

. . . the Taste is not to conform to the Art, but the Art to the Taste.

Joseph Addison, *Spectator*, April 3, 1711

TASTE WAS ONE of the major preoccupations of Georgian England. Virtu—a feeling for, and knowledge of, the fine arts—was considered one of the qualifications of the cultivated man, and a grounding in the arts part of the education of an English gentleman. In his *Discourse on the Dignity, Certainty, Pleasure and Advantage of the Science of a Connoisseur* (1715) Jonathan Richardson Sr. noted the effect which an interest in the fine arts had on the nation by "the reformation of our manners, refinement of our pleasure, and increase of our fortunes and reputation."

Perhaps the most specific embodiment of the idea of taste was the existence of the Society of Dilettanti, whose members had to have made the grand tour, although Horace Walpole sourly remarked that "the nominal qualification for membership is having been in Italy, and the real one being drunk."

This was the age of the grand tour—a phenomenon of inestimable importance in molding attitudes, influencing style, and creating patterns of taste. Usually accompanied by a tutor, the young men on the tour spent several years, sometimes as many as five, taking in many European countries, but concentrating on Italy. Dean Tucker wrote in his highly successful *Instructions for Travellers* of 1757:

> Persons who propose to themselves a Scheme for Travelling generally do it with a view to obtain one or more of the following Ends; viz. First to make Curious Collections, as Natural Philosophers, Virtuosos or Antiquarians. Secondly to improve in Painting, Statuary, Architecture and Music. Thirdly to obtain the reputation of being Men of Vertu and of an elegant Taste.

Adam Smith, embittered by his own experiences as a tutor, complained that he who had been on the grand tour "commonly returns home more conceited, more unprincipled, more dissipated and more incapable of any serious application either to study or business, then he could well have become in so short a time had he lived at home." Yet, the works of art which these widely read, widely traveled young men collected filled the treasure houses of Britain and influenced the Palladian rules of taste in architecture and interior decoration.

It is difficult for us to realize the immense amount of building that went on in England during the eighteenth century. Superbly illustrated pattern books were followed by a spate of builders' manuals which enabled any country gentleman or city tradesman to run up a house or villa with the help of a local housewright. Special prominence was given to specifications for doorways, windows, chimney pieces, and staircases which required detailed draftsmanship. It is this excellence of the parts combined with their harmonious arrangement that distinguishes Georgian architecture. Indeed, the physical remains of the age as a whole are almost uniformly of a refinement of design rarely achieved before or since. Artistic production and consumption blossomed both for the aristocracy and the middle class: the arts and crafts—such as cabinetmaking in the hands of Chippendale and Sheraton or interior decoration under the brothers Adam—reached pinnacles of elegance and delicacy. The statement on Wedgwood's memorial tablet that "he converted a rude and inconsiderable manufacture into an elegant art, and a branch of national commerce" might equally well have been applied to a host of other Georgian craftsmen and manufacturers. If this was the "age of elegance" for the middle class, it was the "age of grandeur" for the aristocracy and gentry.

Robert Morris, himself an author of pattern books, summed up the rationale of the Georgian rule of taste in his *Select Architecture* (1757) when he wrote: "Beauty in all objects, springs from the same unerring Law in Nature, which, in *Architecture*, I would call Proportion." By the time of the French Revolution, British art had evolved from the rule of taste to the rule of liberty; by then the battle lines had been defined on which would be fought in the nineteenth century the war between classicism and romanticism, between sense and sensibility.

Wendell Garrett

The foundation of our Empire was not laid in the gloomy age of Ignorance and Superstition; but at an Epocha when the rights of mankind, after social happiness, were better understood and more clearly defined, than at any former period, the researches of the human mind have been carried to a great extent, the Treasures of knowledge acquired by the labours of Philosophers, Sages and Legislatures, . . . are laid open for our use, and their collected wisdom may be happily applied in the Establishment of our forms of Government. . . . At this auspicious period, the United States came into existence as a Nation, and if their Citizens should not be completely free and happy, the fault will be intirely their own.

George Washington, *Circular Letter to the States*, 1783

Antiques

A FORTUITOUS conjunction of character and destiny two hundred years ago brought America a leadership of philosopher-statesmen unmatched in its history. These men, extraordinary by the standards of their own day and our own, faced the sternest tests confronting our national history—those of achieving independence and building a durable nation. Moreover, there were no precedents for them to follow. As Madison commented to Jefferson in 1789, "We are in a wilderness without a single footstep to guide us. Our successors will have an easier task." They thought of themselves, to use Jefferson's words, as "the Argonauts" who lived in "the Heroic Age." And of them all George Washington knew that he mattered most.

In portraiture and sculpture Washington never smiled. Jean Antoine Houdon's classic bust of a virile hero froze the features in an austere mold, while in Gilbert Stuart's magisterial Athenaeum portrait (frontispiece) Washington is stolid, serious, and unsmiling, intensely self-conscious of his role as hero-president. These were qualities of mind and spirit that later hagiographers and mythmakers described more often than bodily features. The predominant concern of character and intellect over physical appearance was revealed by an author in the *Analectic Magazine* who observed, "Even in their [the patriots'] busts and portraits, we endeavor to trace the lineaments of their minds."

The fundamental element in Washington's character, according to Jefferson, was prudence, followed closely by integrity, honesty, and a stern sense of justice. He was described by contemporaries more in terms of character and intellect than physical appearance. The emphasis was on heroic virtues—self-restraint not self-expression, dignity not forcefulness, moderation not ambition, responsibility to one's accepted duty not making one's mark on the world in novel ways. The occasional references to bodily features simply point to the qualities of mind and spirit. Writers noted a countenance "strongly marked with the lines of thinking," or an eye which not only "kindled with intelligence" but also "spoke the language of an ardent and noble mind."

Washington set his own terms for executive leadership, and a stiff public protocol suited his dignity. He fused the character of his office to the special qualities of his personality, and he lived the role of the hero-president with the profound awareness of a gentleman who was watching his every action as closely as he assumed others were. His stolidity provided a tableau of strength for the new government; just as he protected his own aloofness inside a sturdy case of formalities, so he expected the national executive to stand apart from the nation as a beacon of public order. And for a man of action unsustained by education and wide reading, he turned out in a correct and easy style an incredible amount of writing. Whether recording routine weather and farm data, or maintaining an extensive correspondence, he was a talented phrasemaker ("to bigotry no sanction, to persecution no assistance"), and he was capable of felicitous eloquence in his state papers. When he delivered his first inaugural address in Federal Hall in New York City in 1789, Fisher Ames, the most eloquent member of the First Congress, confessed frankly that he had "sat entranced" in the face of this "allegory in which virtue was personified."

Wendell Garrett

Antiques

We need to recall our own past, to remember our fathers, to remember our heritage. In this present moment of political difficulty let us bear in mind what we owe to those who have gone before us; to the generations that were brought up in this old building . . . that we desire to preserve. We depend at this very moment upon the political sense and sober second-thought, the self-control and readiness in emergencies which in good measure we have inherited from the generations that have gone before us. Let us pay this debt by reverently preserving the shrines of those generations.

Charles W. Eliot speaking at Harvard University, January 18, 1877, in support of the preservation of the Old South Meeting House in Boston

JOHN ADAMS said to his wife in 1780 that he "must study politics and war that my sons may have liberty to study mathematics and philosophy. . . . geography, natural history and naval architecture, navigation, commerce and agriculture, in order to give their children a right to study painting, poetry, music, architecture, statuary, tapestry, and porcelain." But it did not quite work out that way. His son, John Quincy Adams, took up not philosophy but diplomacy, politics, and the presidency. A grandson, Charles Francis Adams, embraced not painting and architecture but law, diplomacy, and Republicanism. And a great-grandson, Charles Francis Adams Jr., took up not poetry and porcelain, but war, law, business—and railroads. "I endeavored to strike out a new path," Charles Francis Jr. said later, "and fastened myself, not, as Mr. Emerson recommends, to a star but to the locomotive-engine." A locomotive engine! Snorting smoke, blowing off steam, and pulling dozens of cars, the "fiery titan" was the tangible symbol of the spirit of free enterprise that prevailed in the 1860's and 1870's with the constant innovations, risky speculations, huge losses, and dizzying profits that, for men like the younger Adams, were a form of intellectual adventure and personal liberation.

Walt Whitman wrote that to understand America one had to appreciate "the pull-down-and-build-over-again spirit," and he fully approved of the constant wrecking of buildings which he witnessed in New York:

> [Take] the choicest edifices to destroy them;
> Room! room! for new far-planning draughtsmen and engineers!
> Clear that rubbish from the building-spots and the paths!

The thought of material progress intoxicated him; he was carried away by the restless—and wasteful—national desire to destroy the old and replace it with the new. And it is true, no other nation has so deliberately and repetitively torn down its buildings of architectural importance and its monuments of irreplaceable value. It was in the teeth of this sort of avarice and expediency that President Charles W. Eliot of Harvard, with Wendell Phillips, James Russell Lowell, Oliver Wendell Holmes, and others banded together in 1877 to arouse the populace against the wanton destruction of the 1729 Old South Meeting House in Boston—the scene of meetings that fomented the American Revolution. The purchase and preservation of the building in the face of impossible odds was an early source of inspiration to preservationists and antiquarians all over the nation.

A new direction in the preservation of our architectural heritage was heralded by the antiquarian William Sumner Appleton, the founder of the Society for the Preservation of New England Antiquities in 1910. His stated purpose was

> to save for future generations structures of the seventeenth and eighteenth centuries, and the early years of the nineteenth, which are architecturally beautiful and unique, or have special historical significance. Such buildings once destroyed can never be replaced.

During the intervening seventy-six years Americans have become convinced that saving old buildings for future generations is a form of progress. Today there are more than fifteen hundred National Historic Landmarks and more than twenty thousand properties of national, state, and local significance listed in the National Register of Historic Places.

We dedicate this issue to the Society for the Preservation of New England Antiquities and its significant accomplishments in the Northeast over the past three-quarters of a century. For "New England is," in David McCord's felicitous words, "the authorized version of America: her land and people chapter and verse for more than 300 years."

Wendell Garrett

Antiques

We may say that the Eighteenth Century, notwithstanding all its Errors and Vices has been, of all that are past, the most honourable to human Nature. Knowledge and Virtues were increased and diffused, Arts, Sciences useful to Men, ameliorating their condition, were improved, more than in any former equal Period.

John Adams to Thomas Jefferson, November 13, 1815

WHILE ALL AGES are ages of transition, there are some in which disruptive and creative forces combine to speed up the normal process of change. In the history of America the eighteenth century is probably the most conspicuous example of such acceleration.

In 1692, during the Salem witchcraft hysteria, the colonial's mind and world were more than half medieval; by 1776 they were more than half modern. This process of change took place against the clash of the old and the new on every side—in science and religion, politics and economics, law and literature, painting and architecture. It was the impact of that quickening, broadening, and emancipating movement of the intellect, which we call the Enlightenment, upon medievalism that gave the age its peculiar character.

It was, for example, in the name of conservatism that the American Revolution—"the most complete, unexpected, and remarkable, of any in the history of nations," in John Adams's words—was conducted. American patriot leaders insisted that they were rebelling not against but on behalf of the principles of the British constitution. Like many of the English writers of social criticism in the Augustan age, they were bitterly hostile to the massive changes taking place in England and the English colonies during the decades following the Glorious Revolution of 1688. Yet the multitude believed neither in change nor in continuity, but was simply disturbed by the violent contrasts around them.

From Cotton Mather to Benjamin Franklin thoughtful men asked, "What do I know?" Sharing the new critical spirit, yet conscious of its destructive power, they sought some valid authority, some ground more firm than that which had served their fathers. It was this intense search that culminated in the foundation of the American republic, tempered by war, discord, and rebellion.

"What then is the American, this new man?" asked Michel Guillaume Jean de Crèvecoeur in his *Letters from an American Farmer* in 1782. The Americans were in the beginning English, soon joined by Scots, Scots-Irish, Dutch, Swedes, French Huguenots, Germans, and the Africans who came as slaves. In the nineteenth century the brew was enriched by more Irish, more Germans, and more Scandinavians, as well as Italians, Poles, Russians, Jews, and Orientals. Transplanted to the New World, the peoples of the Old threw off their national and racial attachments and, by some alchemy, out of the blending of inheritance and historical experience, came a character that could be called American. "The Americans," Walt Whitman wrote, "have the fullest poetical nature."

Eclectic and pluralistic, diverse and dynamic, the American and his household furniture did differ fundamentally from English and European antecedents, as the articles in this issue vividly demonstrate. American furniture suggests something of the wonderful variety of the American crucible in which the base metals of the world were transformed into something new and unified, vindicating the national motto, "*e pluribus unum*."

Wendell Garrett

Antiques

The trade of the East has always been the richest jewel in the diadem of commerce. All nations, in all ages, have sought it; and those which obtained it, or even a share of it, attained the highest degree of opulence, refinement, and power.

Thomas Hart Benton, Speech in the United States Senate, 1847

THE WATERSIDE Yankees of New England were formidable profit-takers. They made money, and lost it, by buying, bartering, smuggling, shipping, and selling whatever commodity turned a profit. They sold cod to the Roman Catholic countries, carried back the heavy wines of the Mediterranean littoral and Atlantic islands, traded sandalwood, *bêche-de-mer*, and sea otter pelts in Canton, and even engaged in the slave trade. However, profits entail risks, and Yankee ships were sunk on coral reefs, lost in tropical storms, burned by disgruntled natives, seized by pirates, and destroyed by British and French men-of-war.

If these New England merchants were economically adventurous, they were politically and intellectually conservative. Emerson's comment that there "was not a book, a speech, a conversation, or a thought" in Massachusetts from 1790 to 1830 worth noticing was harsh, but not wholly inaccurate. Politically their thinking was represented by the most skilled vituperator of the high Federalists, Fisher Ames, who believed the nation was "too big for union, too sordid for patriotism, and too democratic for liberty." In retirement John Adams scorned the Boston merchants' preoccupation with making money. In a letter to his son, John Quincy Adams, he warned against diverting people "from the cultivation of the earth to adventures upon the sea," and accused Boston's merchants of "stiff-rumped stupidity." Nonetheless, the outbreak of war between England and France in 1793 gave these merchants their chance to reap soaring profits as neutral carriers between the warring parties. In their search for new markets and quick returns, New England shipmasters fanned out to ports around the Indian Ocean and in the Pacific on their way to Canton to engage in the China Trade. The impact of the exotic imports from the Far East on Boston, the Athens of America if not the hub of the universe—as Bostonians liked to think of their town—was palpable and startling. Van Wyck Brooks noted: "The Cushing house in Summer Street was surrounded with a wall of Chinese porcelain. Peacocks strutted about the garden. The Chinese servants wore their native dress."

The era of the China Trade is an important chapter in American history, not only for the quantity of goods carried but also for its cross-cultural impact on American and Chinese life. It was a time when Occidental motifs were displayed on Oriental porcelain (see cover), and Chinese ceramic forms were copied by European silversmiths.

The Chinese limited foreign trade to the port of Canton and regulated it through licensed brokers, called hong merchants, who had the monopoly over brokerage with foreign merchants. However, by the early nineteenth century, the system came under increasing strain. The Chinese became alarmed about the inflow of illegal opium from India, not only for the deleterious effects of the drug but also because importing it produced an alarming outflow of silver. The resulting Opium War of 1839–1842 led to a peace settlement that gave the British the entry to trade with China they had wanted, the undeveloped island of Hong Kong, and a large indemnity to be paid in silver dollars. Other treaties followed between China and the United States and other European powers promising most-favored-nation treatment. In effect, the Opium War imposed Western commercial culture on China and made "gunboat diplomacy" more than a figure of speech.

Wendell Garrett

Antiques

When the storm of the French Revolution burst over the different countries of Europe, and shook the foundations of the property of states as well as of individuals, the general distress, and the insecurity of property brought a great number of works of art onto the market, which had for centuries adorned the altars of churches as inviolably sacred, or ornamented the palaces of the great, as memorials of ancient wealth and splendour. Of these works of art England has found means to obtain the most and the best. For scarcely was a country overrun by the French, when English skilled in the arts were at hand with their guineas in their hands.

Gustav Waagan, *Works of Art and Artists in England* (trans. John Murray), 1838

THE FALL of the Bastille—on July 14, 1789—is one of the momentous birthdays of the world. Change was at hand, and the violent birth throes of the French Revolution seemed to be bringing forth a fair child until Jacobin extremism ended with the horrifying spectacle of the guillotine. The eighteenth century, with the faith in progress and the perfectibility of man that characterized the Enlightenment, was over.

Dr. Johnson died in 1784. Sir Joshua Reynolds delivered his last discourse at the Royal Academy in 1790, and died in 1792. The radical John Wilkes retired from public life in 1790. The last part of *The History of the Decline and Fall of the Roman Empire* appeared in 1788, and Edward Gibbon died in 1794, three years before Horace Walpole.

During the transitional years between the French Revolution and 1837, when Victoria came to the throne (and Sir John Soane died), British art and literature fought a war over classicism and romanticism or, as Lord Acton later said in a celebrated aphorism: "two great principles divide the world and contend for the mastery, antiquity and the Middle Ages." And the dualism that these conflicting principles generated—between Athens and Jerusalem, Socrates and Christ, the Doric and the Gothic, and the Greek classics and the Christianity of the Protestant establishment—obsessed early Victorian minds.

Romantic Hellenism had its beginnings in Johann Joachim Winckelmann's *History of Art among the Ancients* (1764), in which the author repudiated the disarray of the rococo by proclaiming that the essence of Greek art lay in "the noble simplicity and the serene greatness of the ancients." And between 1762 and 1795 James ("Athenian") Stuart and Nicholas Revett produced *The Antiquities of Athens, Measured and Delineated*, four sumptuously illustrated volumes which introduced the true nature of Greek genius in art and architecture to the late eighteenth century. As a result, the Roman classical orders derived from those used by Renaissance architects were replaced by the Doric order of the Parthenon and the Ionic of the Erechtheum. The British Museum acquired Sir William Hamilton's collection of Greek vases and bronzes in 1772, thus igniting an interest in the so-called Etruscan style in furniture and interior decoration. Finally, the acquisition in 1816 of the Elgin marbles exerted on artists and architects an influence that persisted until the end of the century. To Keats these fragments of the Parthenon's frieze were "mighty things," mingling "Grecian grandeur with the rude/Wasting of old Time." The cult of ruins was widespread: the idea that archaeological fragments could excite the sensibilities and stimulate the emotions of the beholder (see frontispiece).

There was also a literary dimension to the Greek revival. Dean Gaisford reminded his congregation that the study of Greek literature "not only elevates above the vulgar herd, but leads not infrequently to positions of considerable emolument." Gladstone announced that Homer's world "stands between Paradise and the vices of later heathenism." Walter Pater proclaimed his credo to generations of Oxford undergraduates: "To burn always with this hard, gem-like flame, to maintain this ecstasy, is success in life."

Victorian classicism was a lament for the loss of rural innocence, a jeremiad against the horrors of the Industrial Revolution, a rear guard action against the rising forces of mercantilism and capitalism. To the Victorians Hellas became a sort of heavenly city, a shimmering fantasy beyond the far horizon, a Never-Never Land of myth.

Wendell Garrett

*The Spirit of Enterprize has seized most people & they are making or trying to make Fortunes. Their Attempt will probably have the happy Effect of procuring us many Supplies that we stand in need off [*sic*].*

Robert Morris to William Bingham, Philadelphia, October 20, 1776

PHILADELPHIA was the largest seaport in colonial America by 1760, as well as the leading financial, political, and intellectual center of Revolutionary America. It served as our national capital until 1800, and was generally agreed to be the cleanest, best-governed, healthiest, and most elegant of American cities. "The city of London, though handsomer than Paris, is not so handsome as Philadelphia," Jefferson observed in 1786. Philadelphia had a planned street system, the finest church (Christ Church), the largest public building (Independence Hall), the most bookshops and publishing houses, the greatest number of banks, and the largest public market. It was the center of American scientific and medical study—the influence of the American Philosophical Society (organized for the first time in 1743) and the Philadelphia Medical Society upon science in America can hardly be overestimated.

Between 1765 and 1775 Philadelphia's population increased from about eighteen thousand to nearly twenty-five thousand and by 1800 it was seventy thousand, making Philadelphia the second largest city in the English-speaking world. One immediate result was a building boom. The traveler Charles Janson wrote in 1799 that Philadelphia's buildings were "well built, chiefly of red brick, and in general three stories high. A great number of private houses have marble steps to the street door, and in other respects are finished in a style of elegance."

The city was the home of many different skilled craft groups and a haven for a new merchant class made up of speculative capitalists and aggressive adventurers. And in an increasingly structured social system in which the distance between rich and poor was widening, this patrician elite attempted to demonstrate its power and status not only through elaborate events and exclusive organizations but also through the opulence of their houses and their lavishly carved furniture (cover). One Philadelphia gentleman, for example, was billed for a "carved freeze, folded flowers, birds, etc.," "two dragons for the pediments," a "large flower & ribbon down the corners of the chimney," and "eighteen square flowers in pediments," among other ornaments. The wealthy emulated the patrician conventions of the lesser gentry of Georgian England. As early as mid-century, Peter Kalm, a Swedish visitor, reported (possibly with some exaggeration) that "the English colonies in this part of the world have increased so much in their riches that they almost vie with Old England."

These great men of the Delaware River valley looked to the sea for their opportunities. Forced outside the British system after the Revolution, their ships roamed the Baltic and the Mediterranean, penetrated the markets of China and touched ports in Southeast Asia, explored the fissures in Spain's empire and the cracks in Britain's throughout the Western Hemisphere.

The most successful Philadelphia merchants combined the virtues of the accumulator and the adventurer, on the one hand paring costs, controlling assets, and reinvesting profits instead of consuming them; and on the other hand making imaginative speculations that yielded vast profits. In this climate of heightened risk many of these Philadelphia merchants were induced to venture into novel fields of enterprise, including banking, securities, land speculation, turnpikes, and manufacturing, thereby laying the groundwork for the industrial revolution in America. However, the completion of the Erie Canal in 1825 washed relentlessly at the foundations of Philadelphia's primacy in trade and population. The pursuit of happiness became a race by Philadelphia's merchant class to catch the elusive dream as it was disappearing over the horizon to New York City.

Wendell Garrett

The Congress shall have Power...
To promote the Progress of Science and useful Arts,
by securing for limited Times to
Authors and Inventors the exclusive Right
to their respective Writings and Discoveries.

Constitution of the United States, Article I, Section 8

TWO HUNDRED YEARS ago this month the Constitution was first published—on September 19th, to be exact, in the *Pennsylvania Packet.* During the intensely hot and muggy summer of 1787, the convention delegates worked their way through a flurry of votes and counterproposals, details and compromises (sawing boards to make them fit, as Franklin said).

Likening themselves to the "lawgivers" of ancient times, the leading delegates at Philadelphia shared Madison's conviction that they would "decide forever the fate of republican government." They brought a vast knowledge of history and the long tradition of civic humanism with them to the Convention in May 1787; they departed four months later having fashioned a frame of government that not only redefined the ideology of civic humanism but also introduced a new concept, federalism—variously called divided, or multiple, sovereignty. They dared to believe that the United States could show the world what good government was—a national government elected by, representative of, and responsible to the people.

The framers shared Madison's crucial premise that liberty and order and property must be protected from radical movements and legislative majorities in the states through the careful building of new institutions that were national in scope and power. The delegates were unabashedly pessimistic about the intelligence of the people and the advisability of majority rule. They were conservatives who wanted to curb agrarian radicals and debtors; they were men of property who calculated that their holdings would be safer under a national government judiciously removed from the direct control of the masses. "There is a hearty Puritanism in the view of human nature which pervades the instrument of 1787," observed the British diplomat James, Lord Bryce, in 1888. "It is the work of men who believed in original sin, and were determined to leave open for transgressors no door which they could possibly shut."

It was in checking the excesses of democracy through the separation of powers and the establishment of checks and balances among the three branches of government that the genius of the framers was most sorely tested. But they persevered in their grand "experiment" (a word they often used), retaining for Congress a variety of powers from the Articles of Confederation, and adding new ones, among them the power to grant copyrights and patents.

In its debate on the copyright law the Convention came closest to dealing with matters vital to the arts. As early as 1783 Joel Barlow had sent Madison a copy of the Connecticut copyright statute protecting writers. In August 1787 Madison submitted to a committee of detail a power for Congress to "secure to literary authors their copy rights for a limited time." The version finally approved, although far narrower, promoted and protected "Science and useful Arts" and indicated the close relationship the framers perceived between progress and the creative mind. Constitutional scholars have pointed out that this is the only passage in the entire Constitution (with amendments excepted) in which there is any explicit reference to individual "right" or "rights."

The rich diversity of the American mind, of which the folk art we feature in this issue is one expression, can best be understood in the context of our pluralistic society living under our magisterial Constitution—a society of multiple allegiances, mixed loyalties, divergent economies, different religions, and other interests—which holds the individual citizen in a sort of loose social orbit. Unique in the Western world, we are a nation born of revolt that was moderate, yet genuinely revolutionary; a society that is liberal in its ideals, yet conservative in its behavior, united in its divisions and divided in its unity. *E pluribus unum* was not an idly chosen motto for the new republic. The framers of the Constitution two hundred years ago in Philadelphia rose above petty self-interest and local prejudice to produce what Prime Minister William Gladstone of England called, on the occasion of the Constitution's centennial, "the most remarkable work known to me in modern times to have been produced by the human intellect, at a single stroke (so to speak), in its application to political affairs."

Wendell Garrett

The cause of Liberty *is a cause of too much dignity to be sullied by turbulence and tumult. It ought to be maintained in a manner suitable to her nature. Those who engage in it, should breathe a sedate, yet fervent spirit, animating them to actions of prudence, justice, modesty, bravery, humanity and magnanimity.*

John Dickinson, *Letters from a Farmer in Pennsylvania to the Inhabitants of the British Colonies,* 1768

As sorely divided as the Founding Fathers were with regard to independence (John Dickinson of Delaware voted against the Declaration, yet never considered siding with the Crown against the Colonies), they agreed that the proper ends of government were to protect the people in their lives, liberty, property, and pursuit of happiness. These reluctant Whigs rested their case on English common law and the ancient Saxon rights embodied in the British constitution. As a last resort they appealed to "Laws of Nature and of Nature's God," paying a "decent respect to the opinions of mankind."

These strong, principled men were profoundly learned and articulate, and their dedication to the law gave their revolutionary zeal a distinctive character. They managed to reconcile change and stability, reform and conservation. "Experience must be our only guide," said Dickinson at the Federal Convention. "Reason may mislead us." How tough-minded! How realistic! Reason dictated the logic of their institutions, but experience made them work. And experience they had in abundance.

They read, they pondered, and they wrote. One of the most widely read of their appropriately moderate tracts was *Letters from a Farmer in Pennsylvania to the Inhabitants of the British Colonies* (1768), published serially in the newspaper the year before, about the proper and improper powers of Parliament. Although pacific in tone, the *Letters* pointed out the evils of British policy and suggested force as an ultimate remedy. Despite the pseudonym, which was calculated to win readers, John Dickinson was far from being a farmer. He was an alumnus of the Middle Temple in London, a lapsed Quaker who inherited great wealth, married a Norris from Philadelphia, and had a fine estate outside Dover, Delaware (see pages 820–827). A political conservative, he was well acquainted with the constitutional conflicts of seventeenth-century England and had a talent for seeing both sides of an issue. His Olive Branch Petition to the king in July 1775, professing as it did a fervent loyalty to the Crown and affection for America's ties to Britain, so exasperated the prickly John Adams of Massachusetts that Adams dismissed Dickinson as a "certain great fortune and piddling genius" in a letter to his friend James Warren. The letter, seized by the British, was printed in newspapers, where everyone recognized the "piddling genius" as Dickinson, who was not amused.

In retrospect, one is continually astonished not only by the high literary level of the Founding Fathers' writings but also by the resourcefulness of these men in finding time to write so much. They exhibited a special talent for felicitous phrasemaking, as when Dickinson, collaborating with Jefferson in drafting the "Declaration of the Causes and Necessity for Taking Up Arms," stated "Our cause is just. Our Union is perfect. Our internal Resources are great, and, if necessary, foreign Assistance is undoubtedly obtainable."

The moderate conservatism of what the historian Carl Becker has called the "boldly cautious spirits" like Dickinson who carried through the Revolution rested on fragile assumptions. It depended on a delicate balance of liberty and property, of freedom and order, of reason and passion, of checks and balances that have shown a strange durability in American culture. The checks have really checked and the balances have really balanced: the deep hold on the popular mind of judicial review testifies to that. But more than formal institutions and public documents, what has held this nation together has been a promise made to the world in 1776, reaffirmed in every generation, and eloquently stated by Abraham Lincoln that "the weights should some day be lifted from the shoulders of all men."

Wendell Garrett

There is a natural aristocracy among men.
The grounds for this are virtue and talents.

Thomas Jefferson to John Adams, October 28, 1813

THE PASSING of Charles Carroll of Carrollton on November 14, 1832, marked the end of an era for he was the last of the Signers of the Declaration of Independence. These men were Jefferson's natural aristocrats who thought of themselves as "the Argonauts" who had lived in "the Heroic Age" and brought forth a new nation so conceived that it has long endured.

However, it is a dangerous anachronism to suppose that colonial America was a democracy, or was struggling toward democracy in the modern sense. Not so. Colonial values and politics were indebted to the norms of Hanoverian England—a highly structured Christian monarchy grounded in a landed aristocracy. In Massachusetts not only did the founders belong to Britain's landed gentry, but as good Puritans they considered their superior station divinely ordained. In the words of their first governor, John Winthrop, "God Almightie in his most holy and wise providence hath soe disposed of the Condicion of mankinde, as in all times some must be rich some poore, some highe and emminent in power and dignitie; others mean and in subieceion."

As the years went on the aristocracy retained its primacy and families with fortunes newly made on land and sea won admittance to the circle of the ruling elite. The Virginia patrician William Fitzhugh spoke for the Southern aristocracy in avowing that his children had "better be never born than ill-bred." To William Byrd II it was nothing short of a "tragical Story" when a well-born Virginia girl in 1732 played "so senceless a Prank" as to marry her uncle's overseer, "a dirty Plebian."

The gentry was also distinguished by the elegance of their clothing and furniture. The traveler Joseph Bennett wrote in 1740 of Boston, "both the ladies and gentlemen dress and appear as gay, in common, as courtiers in England on a coronation or birthday." William Eddis, after a few years in Annapolis, wrote in 1771 that he was "almost inclined to believe" that a new mode spread more rapidly among "polished and affluent" Americans than among "many opulent" Londoners. Also in 1771 Charles Carroll of Carrollton ordered a complete set of furniture from his London agent for a room in his Annapolis house. Included were two handsome gilded girandoles of two lights each, four crimson curtains, one fashionable sofa with twelve chairs to match, two pier glasses "to be as fashionable and handsome as can be purchased for fifteen guineas each. The carving and guilding to conform with the girandoles. . .to be of a solid kind, it has been found by experience that slight carving will neither endure the extremes of heat or cold nor the rough treatment of negro servants."

The colonial leadership was an oligarchy whose members asked voters to embrace their politics as well as their social superiority and superior judgment. This governing aristocracy possessed the wisdom and capacity to provide cultural leadership and set standards of taste through its patronage of artists and craftsmen.

To be sure, in the events foreshadowing the final crisis of the American Revolution loyalties were divided, and some of the colonial gentry sided ardently with Britain, or at least sought to prevent an irreparable break. However, the well-informed Thomas McKean, himself a Signer, wrote John Adams in retrospect that almost two-thirds of the country's "influential characters" had favored the American cause. In spite of contested elections, noisy rhetoric, and competing factions, when the war finally broke out the Continental Congress unanimously chose a Virginia aristocrat as commander in chief of the armed forces, and in due course a grateful republic named him its first president.

The revolt against upper-class dominance came with the passing of the founding fathers, and the fragile consensus of a deferential society in America was destroyed under the impact of Jacksonian democracy.

Wendell Garrett

It is a fact not generally realized that the American Philosophical Society at Philadelphia, the Royal Society of Great Britain and the Royal Institution of London, are all of them in a measure indebted for their birth and first foundation to natives or inhabitants of New England.

Jacob Bigelow, *North American Review*, 1816

THE INITIAL CELEBRATION of America's prospects in the arts and sciences seems to have coincided with the end of the French and Indian War in 1763. Delivering a sermon in Newport, Rhode Island, Ezra Stiles declared, "Not only science, but the elegant Arts are introducing apace, and in a few years we shall have... Painting, Sculpture, Statuary. . .and greek Architecture in considerable Perfection among us." When Benjamin Franklin wrote his friend Mary Stevenson in London in 1763 " 'tis said, the Arts delight to travel Westward," he was reiterating a theory that had its roots in classical antiquity, remained an important tenet for scholars throughout the Renaissance, and was reaffirmed during the eighteenth-century Enlightenment by prophets of progress who were convinced that the North American continent was destined to become the future habitat for the arts and sciences.

A belief in the utility and promise of Newtonian science permeated the thinking of all ranks and classes of Americans, mainly for its usefulness in navigation, the physical sciences, medicine, agriculture, astronomy, meteorology, geology, and the invention of mechanical devices. The early settlers were acquainted with the uses of water and wind power, building grist, saw, and fulling mills on the many fast-flowing streams along the Northeast fall line. Nathaniel Bowditch, the self-taught New England mathematical genius, corrected thousands of errors in the most widely used navigational guides and in at least fifty-six editions of his own *New American Practical Navigator*. The ingenuity and imagination of the colonial metalworker Shem Drowne, who hammered out the celebrated copper grasshopper weather vane for Boston's Faneuil Hall (frontispiece), is evident in the beauty of this early mobile and in its usefulness as a scientific instrument. In 1680 Thomas Brattle of Boston contributed some astronomical observations to the English Royal Society, which Newton used in his *Principia*. John Winthrop, who held the Hollis chair of mathematics and natural philosophy at Harvard College, observed a transit of Mercury and a lunar eclipse in 1740, which he reported to the Royal Society; in 1761 he observed the important transit of Venus across the sun's disk; and in 1766 he became a fellow of the Royal Society. Since unorthodox views about dissection crept in with the advance of anatomy and surgery, and since dissection was not legalized in Massachusetts until 1831, some Harvard students in the classes of 1770 to 1772, including John Warren, formed their own anatomical society which met secretly to dissect dogs and cats. But it was Franklin who, by the middle of the eighteenth century, was conceded to be one of the two or three great scientific minds of the world, a theoretician, experimenter, and inventor who wrested the fire from heaven and the scepter from the tyrants, as Jean Le Rond d'Alembert declared. In the next generation Thomas Jefferson attained eminence as the best-known American intellectual, familiar to philosophers and scientists of every land. To him the pursuit of scientific knowledge was man's most important quest. "There is," he once wrote, "not a sprig of grass that shoots uninteresting to me."

While Winthrop was observing the planets and Warren was dissecting dogs, homesteaders throughout New England were tinkering, improving, inventing. They were confident and self-reliant craftsmen short on book learning but long on know-how, exceptionally flexible workbench artisans who moved readily from making furniture to erecting textile machinery and ultimately to fashioning parts for steam engines; from building houses to constructing paper mills; from working for wages to becoming entrepreneurs. These versatile traits were transmitted from generation to generation more by observation and practice than by formal apprenticeship or schooling, resulting in a flexible labor supply of high competence. These achievements were the proof of John Adams's observation to Benjamin Rush early in the nineteenth century: "There is nothing. . .more ancient in my memory than the observation that arts, sciences, and empire have travelled westward. . .that their next leap would be over the Atlantic into America."

Wendell Garrett

. . . the main spur to Trade, or rather to Industry and Ingenuity, is the exorbitant Appetites of Men, which they will take pains to gratifie, and so be disposed to work, when nothing else will incline them to it; for did Men content themselves with bare Necessaries, we should have a poor World.

Sir Dudley North, *Discourses upon Trade,* 1691

The Glorious Revolution of 1688 was a swift, aristocratic coup that came unexpectedly upon a nation enjoying unprecedented prosperity and social tranquility. For the great majority of Tories and Anglican clergy, with their belief in the divine right of kings, it was a trauma. The expectation that the Roman Catholic James II—who had endeavored "to subvert and extirpate the protestant religion, and the laws and liberties of this kingdom"—might submit to the prince of Orange's army and abide by the wishes of Parliament were shattered by his flight to France. Hopes that James's titular rights might be preserved by the fiction of a regency, or that William of Orange might even act as a consort to his wife, Princess Mary (the eldest child of James II), proved equally vain. William would accept nothing less than the crown itself for life, sharing the title but not the power with his wife as the queen consort, even though her claim to the throne was manifestly superior.

James II's replacement by his difficult Dutch son-in-law in February 1689 was one of the most decisive changes of monarchs in English history. James had been devotedly Catholic and narrowly English, hostile to the pretensions of Parliament, and impatient with the restrictions that the laws imposed on his power. William III, although James's nephew by blood, was anything but English in his ways. While he indulged his wife's Anglicanism, his sympathies lay with the Calvinism of the Dutch Reformed Church, his favorite friends were as foreign as his accent, his intelligence was acute, and his tastes cosmopolitan. While he had no great love of representative institutions, he had learned to live with them in the United Provinces and accepted the fact that he had to do so in England.

Fortunately for William, Mary was personally popular—which he was not—and was devoted to the established church. After she died childless in December 1694, those who became disillusioned with William began to form an alternative court around his sister-in-law Anne. William did not remarry, and Anne's numerous unsuccessful pregnancies are legendary; her only surviving child died in 1700. The Act of Settlement in 1701 named the Hanoverians as successors to Anne.

England after the Glorious Revolution was a world of sensational plots and continuous turbulence, of corruption and factional fighting. Yet it blossomed into one of the wealthiest nations in the world, displacing the Netherlands as the chief trading nation, with London a serious rival to Amsterdam as the banking capital of the world. Augustan England of the late seventeenth and the eighteenth centuries was intensely self-aware and proud of its achievements. Isaac Newton and John Locke were the intellectual giants in a constellation of original thinkers exploring new regions of knowledge.

Augustan society, prosperous and aesthetically aware, developed a passion for luxury. The intellectual origins of a "consumer revolution" began in the 1690's. A taste for colorful printed-cotton fabrics imported by the East India Company reached epidemic proportions. As early as 1697 Celia Fiennes found a rich tradesman in Bury Saint Edmunds who had two rooms "full of china," and by 1714 "the humour. . .of furnishing houses with china ware" was widely indulged, to the prejudice, it was said, of many a family's budget. Daniel Defoe, writing during George I's reign, complained that the appetite for emulation impelled even "mean" tradesmen to "have their parlours set off with the tea-table and. . .the silver coffee pot." William III brought many old master paintings with him from Holland, and the collecting of pictures rapidly became fashionable. One contemporary recalled in the 1720's "how all Europe has been rummaged, as we may say, for pictures to bring over hither, where, for twenty years, they yielded the purchasers—such as collected them for sale—immense profit." Despite two exhausting wars and complaints over heavy taxation, the author of the *Complete English Tradesman* could write in 1727, "we see more new houses at this time in England, built within twenty to forty years, than were built in England in two hundred years before."

According to Bernard de Mandeville's famous allegory of English society, *The Grumbling Hive: or, Knaves Turn'd Honest* (1705), the whole hive was "Slave to Prodigality/That Noble Sin; whilst Luxury/ Employ'd a Million of the Poor,/And odious Pride a Million More." The remarkably hostile reception to Mandeville's allegory from the press, the pulpit, and the courts suggests how great a threat to social control was the current collecting mania and love of display held to be.

The contents of this issue grew out of the exhibition entitled *Courts and Colonies: The William and Mary Style in Holland, England and America* that will be on view at the Cooper-Hewitt Museum in New York City until February 12, 1989, and then will be seen at the Carnegie Museum of Art in Pittsburgh, Pennsylvania, from March 18 to May 28, 1989.

Wendell Garrett

Do you call this a Republic? . . . I know of no Republic in the world, except America, which is the only country for such men as you and I. It is my intention to get away from this place as soon as possible. . . . I have done with Europe and its slavish politics.

Thomas Paine, 1802

The American and French revolutions had a great deal in common: both were democratic revolutions against government by any established, privileged, closed, or self-recruiting group; both were the birth throes of new political systems first designed to express individualism in social life; both stood for popular sovereignty, the rights of man, no taxation without representation, suspicion of established religion, republicanism, and nationalism.

There were also great differences between the two revolutions. In America not a single person was executed for political crimes between 1776 and 1783, whereas in France the execution of Louis XVI prefigured the demise not only of his supporters but also of his confirmed enemies during the Reign of Terror of 1793 and 1794. While Americans created a pluralistic ideology that successfully balanced the liberty of each citizen within the sovereignty of the nation, France stumbled from bloodbath to republic to empire and back to monarchy. In 1789 General Washington chose to become a modern Cincinnatus—America's first constitutional president. In 1804 the Corsican General Bonaparte appeared as a romanticized emperor of the French.

By 1776 American republicans were politically bold beyond any other people. Some of the shared traits of radical Whig ideology and American Puritanism created the idea of a single chosen people destined for a single mission. "God sifted a whole Nation that he might send Choice Grain over into this Wilderness," as one of the Puritan elect put it in 1670. By 1776 the radical Whig perception of politics provided not only the vocabulary but also the grammar of thought for the men and women who wanted independence. Orators like Patrick Henry developed a new, more emotional, more accessible rhetoric—the secular analogue of the religious revivalists. Thomas Paine's pamphlet *Common Sense* became a best seller within months of publication: plainly written and studded with familiar biblical references, Paine's ungrammatical tract best expressed what Americans thought they were doing and pronounced it a divinely sanctioned cause.

Americans who had considered themselves dutiful colonial subjects of a British king declared themselves citizens of a new world. "But why send an American youth to Europe for education?" asked Jefferson in 1785. "It appears to me then that an American coming to Europe for his education loses in his knowledge, in his morals, in his health, in his habits, and in happiness." After 1776 Britain, which had been a mother, became a malicious stepmother, and the king, a failed father. In the self-image of the revolutionary generation Americans were moral and the British were immoral and corrupt. Jefferson caught the spirit of it when he wrote "The preservation of the holy fire is confided to us by the world, and the sparks which will emanate from it will ever serve to rekindle it in other quarters of the globe."

While radical Whigs and the Puritan fathers had, in theory, despised trade and commerce because it quickened greed, the American revolutionaries of the 1780's had to accept the prospect of a commercially prosperous, if still virtuous, republic. In America the struggle for home rule, which never became a social conflict, survived into an age of high capitalism because it was transformed into an important part of the hopeful American world view—at once Jeffersonian, democratic, individualistic, and genuinely liberal.

In France the failed revolution generated a hostile class consciousness on the left and exacerbated traditionalist resistance on the right. That double legacy has affected French history for two hundred years. As Karl Marx wrote, men make their history, but they do not make it as they please. "The traditions of all the dead generations," he wrote, "weigh like a nightmare on the brains of the living."

Wendell Garrett

I bade adieu to Mount Vernon, to private life, and to domestic felicity, and with a mind oppressed with more anxious and painful sensations than I have words to express, set out for New York. . .with the best disposition to render service to my country in obedience to its calls, but with less hope of answering its expectations.

George Washington's diary, April 16, 1789

Artists, contemporaries, and later myth makers froze George Washington in the classic image of the selfless patriot-statesman—tight-lipped and determined, proper if not priggish. His great height, dignity, and faith in himself and his country fixed upon the public the notion of Washington as a man devoid of deep affections and passions, aloof, austere, and impenetrably reserved.

Fisher Ames, the Federalist orator, likened Washington to Epaminondas, the Theban patriot, whose nobility of character Plutarch eulogized. Washington himself seemed to prefer the role of Cincinnatus, the virtuous Roman and sensible husbandman. "Agriculture has ever been the most favorite amusement of my life," he wrote after his Revolutionary campaigns were done. Sowing and reaping, planting and grafting, and riding along his fields of green tobacco and rippling grain were his chief delights.

Architecture was his favorite art, and in designing Mount Vernon he obeyed no guide but his own eye. Few historic houses in America so directly reflect the mind and character of their builder and occupant. Mount Vernon was a huge estate that stretched some ten miles along the Potomac River and penetrated inland about four miles at its widest point. Even as Washington—the living symbol of the Revolutionary cause—was much more than a country squire, Mount Vernon was vastly more than a country gentleman's residence. With no permanent national capital and no president's house, Mount Vernon was one of the most prominent buildings in America and the scene of impressive entertaining for renowned visitors. It could be "compared to a well-resorted tavern," so Washington wrote, "as scarcely any strangers who are going from north to south or from south to north do not spend a day or two at it." To intimates whom he invited for long visits he warned: "My manner of living is plain. I do not mean to be put out of it. A glass of wine and bit of mutton are always ready, and such as will be content to partake of them are welcome. Those who expect more will be disappointed, but no change will be affected by it." The American Cincinnatus embraced the Horatian ideal of the good life: cultivation of the soil and tranquil repose by the hearth.

Washington is beyond question one of the greatest men in history, one of the noblest men who ever lived. He is the towering figure in the establishment of the United States, and he did more than any other man to create and preserve the Republic. "Washington was more than a military leader: he was the eagle, the standard, the flag, the living symbol of the cause," in James Thomas Flexner's words. Able and energetic, he had many virtues. He was also impulsive, vulnerable, and fallible. Gouverneur Morris, an intimate friend, wrote of Washington that few men "had to contend with passions so violent." His path through life was studded with mistakes, indiscretions, resentments, and the exaggerated complaints common to human kind; but he also manifested lofty patriotism, dedication, idealism, modesty, self-mastery, and unselfish service to the state. It is questionable if another man in all of American history has ever been so venerated by his compatriots as the "godlike Washington," as Americans came to call him. A military man but never a militarist, it is not Washington the victor at Yorktown who stirs the deepest appeal, but the legendary Washington on his knees in the snow at Valley Forge. He was great because he was good. The most famous summary of Washington's career was spoken by Henry ("Light-Horse Harry") Lee in a memorial address delivered two days after the former president died: "First in war, first in peace, first in the hearts of his countrymen, he was second to none in the humble and endearing scenes of private life. . .the purity of his private character gave effulgence to his public virtues."

Wendell Garrett

The cause of America is in a great measure the cause of all mankind.

Thomas Paine, *Common Sense*, 1776

As the citizens of France and America first came into contact with each other on the eve of the American Revolution, French *philosophes* were carried away in their enthusiasm. "We have been accused of being prejudiced in favor of these Americans," wrote the editors of the *Ephémérides du citoyen* in their review of John Dickinson's *Letters from an American Farmer in Pennsylvania*, adding in justification, "The character of this flourishing nation, of this beautiful land peopled by three million happy men, can give us some idea of the dignity of which the human race is capable."

Benjamin Franklin's first visit to Paris in 1767 was the catalyst which started the fermentation of Americanism there. Franklin became a veritable Johnny Appleseed, planting seeds of the American dream across the fields of Europe. Then the war brought appreciable numbers of other Americans to France, among them John Adams, Thomas Jefferson, Silas Deane, Arthur Lee, Thomas Paine, and John Paul Jones. These men, who returned from France with the furniture and furnishings we feature in this issue, somehow came to symbolize for the French a people and a place in which men could dwell together in universal liberty and equality. A fairly common French interpretation of American culture was the Greek-colony concept: America was not to be a new and different civilization, but rather a second Syracuse, a colonial extension of European culture. "It is perhaps in America that the human race is to be recreated," Louis Mercier wrote in 1778, ". . . that it is to perfect the arts and sciences, that it is to recreate the nations of antiquity." America was for the French "the hope of the human race" because she furnished the chance to prove for all time the basic assumption of the idea of progress: to prove that man, once granted the free use of his enlightened reason, could not fail to create a golden age of prosperity, justice, and happiness.

Although the American and French revolutions were roughly contemporaneous and inspired by the same ideals, the society and cultural life of each country followed utterly different trajectories. Americans believed that the mindless bloodiness of the Great Terror of 1793–1794 betrayed the stability, consensus, and conservatism that characterized the American Revolution. The counter-revolution of Thermidor, which in July 1794 overthrew Robespierre, marked the end of the American dream in France and brought to a close one of the great moments of fraternal cooperation in Franco-American relations.

Differences between France and America became exaggerated with the passage of time during the nineteenth century. While France was Roman Catholic, America was overwhelmingly Protestant. France's emphasis on paternalism, national glory, and appreciation of culture contrasted sharply with American advocacy of self-reliance and adventurous enterprise. Frenchmen were inclined to philosophize, to change their government frequently, and to look backwards. Americans tended to be practical, to treasure political stability, and to look ahead. Yet, in spite of cultural differences, there has long been a sentimental attachment between the two nations. Even when they have suffered a deterioration of diplomatic relations, the cross-fertilization of tastes and ideas has profoundly enriched the cultural lives of the "sister republics." We Americans, in particular, have inherited the authority of French culture in letters, fashion, food, art, and architecture.

Wendell Garrett

I think that to be an American is an excellent preparation for culture. We have exquisite qualities as a race, and it seems to me that we are ahead of the European races in the fact that more than either of them we can deal freely with forms of civilisation not our own, can pick and choose and assimilate and in short (aesthetically etc.) claim our property wherever we find it.

Henry James to Thomas Sergeant Perry, 1867

THE AMBITION of Henry James—the lonely aesthete—was to harness and transcend three cultures: the French, the British, and the American. Dislocated from the American scene by his self-imposed exile of more than a quarter century, he ceaselessly patrolled the Anglo-American frontier. He attempted to extend to the novel the principles Matthew Arnold had applied to poetry, and, as an American, he hoped to fulfill the promise held out by Nathaniel Hawthorne. In the summer of 1879, when the Europeanized James wrote *Hawthorne* in London, he touched a sensitive nerve among his contemporaries by seeming to suggest that American culture was too aridly provincial to nourish a great artist. His famous catalogue of all the "items of high civilization" missing from American life ("No State. . . .No sovereign, no court, no personal loyalty, no aristocracy, no church, no clergy. . .no sporting class—no Epsom nor Ascot!") was an indictment of "the coldness, the thinness, the blankness" of American society in which Hawthorne grew to maturity. His *Hawthorne* was in part a defense of his own recent move to England, in part an implied judgment that his novels would benefit from the rich texture of Europe, and in part a literary son's declaration of independence from a profoundly influential father. But James also knew, as he wrote in a letter in 1872, that "it's a complex fate, being an American, and one of the responsibilities it entails is fighting against a superstitious valuation of Europe."

James's fiction asks what happens to Americans in Europe and what happens to Europeans under the impact of Americans. He set the two societies he knew against each other for balance and contrast in works that thrive on paradox and ambiguity. For James London was to live in, Paris to learn in, Italy to love, and America a sounding board for his literary sensibility.

James was one of a host of American writers and painters who crossed the Atlantic during the gilded age to seek inspiration and learn from European teaching. Some were dissenters and rebels working on the margins of highbrow culture, while others of substantial means and from privileged social positions explored their common humanity in the classical English literary tongue and fashionable portraiture. One of the latter was Mary Cassatt, a cultivated gentlewoman from Philadelphia with no trace of bohemianism in either her habits or her attitudes. She overrode her wealthy parents' objections and went to Paris to study art. There she worked with Degas and became an established member of the impressionists. Even though she spent virtually her entire professional career abroad, this proper spinster, who found a vicarious motherhood in her glowing depictions of women and their small children, remained "exclusively of her people," as one French critic observed. "Hers," he added, "is a direct and significant expression of the American character."

Among the positive aspects of that character which James included in his glum list of America's deficiencies in *Hawthorne* were the gift of humor and the ability to have realized "immense uninterrupted development." And he added, with words borrowed from Hawthorne himself, "When one thinks of the scale on which it took place, of the prosperity that walked in its train and waited on its course, of the hopes it fostered and the blessings it conferred," one was bound to speak of it as a time of "broad morning sunshine" in which "all went forward" in an "earthly empire." And who can deny, in comparison with all other nations and empires that have ever existed, that America is a country indeed bathed "in broad morning sunshine"?

Wendell Garrett

This new people, when they had it in their power to change all their laws, to throw themselves upon any Utopian theory that the folly of a wild philanthropy could devise, to discard as abominable every vestige of English rule and English power . . . did not do so, but preferred to cling to things English.

Anthony Trollope, *North America,* 1862

EVEN IN colonial times Americans were far more impressed by local diversities than by similarities among the several regions of British America. In 1760 Benjamin Franklin informed British readers in a well-known pamphlet that no two of the separate colonies on the North American continent seemed to be much alike. Rather, Franklin emphasized, the colonies were "not only under different governors, but have different forms of government, different laws, different interests, and some of them different religious persuasions and different manners." Significant regional divergencies remained so strong after independence that the writer W. H. Gardner asked as late as 1822 whether any New England reader ever crossed the Potomac or the Hudson without feeling himself "surrounded by a different race of men?"

One of the central assumptions in the study of the American arts is this enhanced sense of regional differences in the products made by colonial craftsmen. Yet in their retelling of our history, some modern historians have demonstrated convincingly that variations within America were far less important than the similarities that made American culture different from that of England and Europe. They argue that Americans of the revolutionary generation found it possible to think of themselves as part of a shared culture that transcended sectional differences. Few would have found incredible George Washington's assertion in his Farewell Address of 1796 that "with slight shades of difference," Americans had "the same religion, manners, habits, and political principles." In mounting and carrying out a successful war of independence they had "in a common cause fought and triumphed together." Most citizens of the new republic found comfort in viewing themselves as fundamentally different from their European progenitors. They thought of themselves as members of a liberal society, born free and happily devoid of feudal traditions and class distinctions, devoted to individual expression, social mobility, pragmatic self-interest, and the protection of property rights.

Generalizations about what is characteristically American about American culture in general, and the American arts in particular, are difficult because they pose a riddle of both logic and history: logically, how can we speak of America as a civilization whole and unique within itself, and at the same time assert, as Anthony Trollope did, that the legacy of British culture was decisive in the formative years of the Republic? Historically, how has America developed out of the common conditions of the modern world, yet developed with such an acceleration of energy and power?

"Our ancestors sought a new continent," said James Russell Lowell; "What they found was a new condition of mind." And it is in the speculative operations of the mind that Americans have attempted to give ideological coherence to understanding the riddle of America. To this end they have contributed both unorganized beliefs transmitted from generation to generation as superstitions and folklore, and systematized theology, philosophy, and law.

Long ago Tocqueville examined "the most perfect" Constitution of the United States, and concluded that "the Union is an ideal nation, which exists, so to speak, only in the mind, and whose limitations and extent can only be discerned by the understanding." This conception of America insists on the continuing presence of intellect as the primary source of national definition. The Founding Fathers had faith in legal thought as *ordo ordinans,* the ordering order that arranges values in meaningful patterns. Their decision "to form a more perfect Union" was an act of the imagination that must be shared if it is to be renewed.

Wendell Garrett

Against the assault of laughter, nothing can stand.

Mark Twain, *The Mysterious Stranger,* 1916

Mark Twain—whom William Dean Howells memorably termed the Lincoln of our literature—celebrated humor as mankind's supreme weapon against follies, foibles, and fools. Twain, who caricatured himself as one of the "phunny phellows," once thought of becoming a preacher, but lacking, as he said, "the necessary stock in trade—*i.e.,* religion," he yielded to "a 'call' to literature, of a low order—i.e., humorous." This majestic, white-maned foe of humbug endures because he was more than a cracker-barrel philosopher or vernacular humorist. He gave his countrymen pride in themselves, their humor, and their literature. His favorite methods were understatement and exaggeration, incongruity and hyperbole, tall tales and regional dialect. Who can forget, for example, bragging Bob and the Child of Calamity in *Life on the Mississippi*? "Look at me! I take nineteen alligators and a bar'l of whiskey for breakfast when I'm in robust health, and a bushel of rattlesnakes and a dead body when I'm ailing! . . . Whoo-oop! Stand back and give me room according to my strength! Blood's my natural drink, and the wail of the dying is music to my ear!"

That there are differences between the American comic spirit and that of other nations has long been recognized. As long ago as 1838 a puzzled Englishman in the *London and Westminster Review* wrote: "The curiosity of the public regarding the peculiar nature of American humor seems to have been early satisfied with the application of the all-sufficing word exaggeration." Then, as now, burlesque and the tall tale were our gifts to comic literature.

In democratic America the social distance between people was suspended, and the lofty and the lowly, the sacred and the profane, the great and the insignificant, were yoked together with jolly relativity, creating "a language utterly unknown to the prose or verse of this country," as a contributor to the *Edinburgh Review* wrote in 1809—a language distinguished by the introduction of "a great multitude of words which are radically and entirely new" and by "the perversion of a still greater number of words from their proper use or signification." For Tocqueville linguistic innovation was endemic to democratic culture. He noted that Americans "often mix their styles in an odd way," as "the continual restlessness of democracy leads to endless change in language." By often "giving double meanings to one word," Tocqueville argued, "democratic peoples often make both the old and the new significations ambiguous," so that "the phrase is left to wander." In other words, political and social freedom were reflected in linguistic freedom which stripped words of their normal associations and left them to float in space. It is this quality of democratic language that impelled the nineteenth-century Protestant theologian Horace Bushnell to argue (like a precursor of Jacques Derrida and today's deconstructionists) that words are "inexact representations of thought" and "it follows that language will be ever trying to mend its own deficiencies, by multiplying its forms of representation."

The first American humorist whose writings reveal the linguistic changes created by democratic mass culture was Washington Irving. He taught the great lesson of American humor: that one could point out the turbulent excesses of American democracy while at the same time distancing oneself from them and thus stripping them of their terror. In *Salmagundi* (1807–1808) it is not Irving who expresses distress over the "orgies of liberty"; rather, it is the ridiculously named Mustapha Rub-A-Dub Keli Khan, a prejudiced Oriental visitor, who is appalled by "scenes of confusion, of licentious disorganization" in a presidential election, which he says gives rise to complete irresponsibility in the popular press, with "individuals verbally massacred, families annihilated by whole sheets full, and slang-whangers cooly bathing their pens in ink, and rioting in the slaughter of their thousands."

By using a variety of comic voices Irving provided himself with a kind of artistic haven from which to draw attention to the chaotic character of American popular culture. This detachment from any single viewpoint, and his studied slipperiness when it came to the meaning of words created humor out of the playful subversion of linguistic referentiality and undermines the whole notion of a mimetic language system referring directly to perceived reality.

No single generalization can describe the American brand of humor, which has acted as a catalyst at every stage of our awkward and uneven growth, pointing out our extravagances and our incongruities and helping us to appreciate our common humanity.

Sir Walter Scott explained to Washington Irving that the character of a nation is to be found in its plain people since the gentry are much alike everywhere. Our national humor has thrived on the folklore of the plain people, often crude and cruel, sometimes racist and sexist, but nearly always sympathetic, kind, and wise, encompassing the Yankee peddler, the frontiersman in deerskin shirt and coonskin cap, the Southern cracker, the Negroes, the Irish, and the Jews. It has taken innumerable literary forms, from the fable, anecdote, and tall tale, to the parlor farce, light verse, and the playful retelling of classical legend. It has not been afraid of dialect or slang; it has been democratic and has made us one. We laughed as we grew.

Wendell Garrett

It seems as one grows older,
That the past has another pattern, and ceases to be a mere sequence—
Or even development: the latter a partial fallacy
Encouraged by superficial notions of evolution,
Which becomes, in the popular mind, a means of disowning the past.

T. S. Eliot, *The Four Quartets,* 1943

THE CONCEPT of progress as a benevolent evolutionary process—the notion that all history can be seen as a gradual, but continuous ascent to a given end—was once described by the English historian J. B. Bury as "the animating and controlling idea" of modern Western civilization. In the eighteenth century and far into the nineteenth, eminent men of letters and utopian dreamers looked upon the future of mankind with optimism. They had a sanguine faith that now men could indeed become gods. Anne Robert Jacques Turgot, the founding philosopher of progress, went so far as to declare in 1778 that America was "the hope of the human race." Voltaire, in his *Philosophical Letters,* declared America the improvement of all that was excellent in England; the Quakers of Pennsylvania, he asserted, had already created "that golden age of which men talk." And the marquis de Condorcet wrote (as Jefferson might have written), "There will come a time ... when the sun will behold henceforth on earth free men only, recognizing no master but their own reason." If the year 1776 was made notable by Adam Smith's and Edward Gibbon's classics, it was also made historic by the Declaration of Independence, permeated as it is with its drafter's faith in human progress.

To the nineteenth century, heaven on earth was possible, and utopia was propounded by eminent men of letters as a legitimate hope—a hope embodied in America in more than a hundred experimental communities based on communalism, celibacy, free love, intellectual exercise combined with physical toil, religious devotion, industry, education, or intellectual isolation. But by the end of the century doubt had taken over; the bright promise of the future was riven by nostalgia for a pastoral past. Humans were being diminished, degraded by specialization, dislocated by urbanization, and disillusioned by the erosion of the old democratic tradition in new social conditions. Henry James was "frankly bewildered by the turmoil in American life"; Edith Wharton found herself "unfitted for the broils of modern life"; and Santayana confessed to being oppressed with a sense of "despair over modern life." Mark Twain and Henry Adams gloomily contrasted America at the end of the century with the pre-Civil War America of their youth. On canvas, the sylvan landscapes of the Hudson River school painters were an a priori complaint against the smoke and noise of railroads and factories. Frederic Remington and Charles Russell immortalized their cowboys and Indians only after the frontier had vanished and the winning of the West was a memory. Isolated and lonely, those fearful of the future became obsessed by nostalgia for their recollected images of the past.

T. S. Eliot responded to the social disorder of his own time with an almost irrational rage for order and with a strong plea for the necessity of a remembered past—a past represented by ritual, tradition, memory, and even myths. When he was buried in the Somerset, England, village of East Coker, the home of his seventeenth-century ancestor who migrated to the New World, lines from *East Coker,* the second of the *Four Quartets,* were inscribed on his memorial tablet to reflect his own history and strong sense of the past: "In my beginning is my end" and "In my end is my beginning." Eliot was the product of two cultures, one native and one adopted, both threatened by the dislocation and turmoil of war that drove him to his meditation on the personal and historical past. Throughout the history of the American people, a deep-running tide of nostalgia has always paralleled the idea of progress. Like the god Janus, we face both the future and the past.

Wendell Garrett

The only way for us to become great and, if possible, inimitable is through imitation of the ancients....The general and predominant mark of Greek masterpieces is noble simplicity and calm grandeur.

Johann Joachim Winckelmann, *History of Ancient Art*, 1764

IN THE EIGHTEENTH CENTURY, every aspect of the known universe and every realm of human activity was discussed, analyzed, or questioned: the principles of science and the foundations of morality, the education of children and the punishment of criminals, the duties of princes and the rights of man. Many predicted the triumph of reason and humanity enshrined in Diderot's *Encyclopédie*, and the abolition of prejudice, superstition, ignorance, and injustice. Yet in 1759 the *philosophe* d'Alembert acknowledged that the consequence of the intellectual ferment of his time was "to throw new light on some subjects and a new shadow on others, just as the effect of the ebb and flow of the sea is to cast some objects on the shore and to carry others away."

Paradoxically, or perhaps consequentially, this historically minded age, with the exception of Edward Gibbon's *Decline and Fall of the Roman Empire*, produced little profound and original historical scholarship. And it seems odd that in an age of intellectual turmoil art was so apparently restrained, astringent, and formal, concerned less with the human spirit than with archaeological exactitude.

But neoclassicism—the cult of antiquity—was more than a nostalgic obsession with the past; the movement had a revolutionary character and serious purpose that Baudelaire recognized when he wrote that the great goal of the neoclassicists "consisted in reaction against an excess of gay and charming frivolities...and that they marched by the light of their artificial sun with a frankness, a resolution and an *esprit de corps* worthy of true party men."

Neoclassicism was a cerebral movement, as Winckelmann declared, in which the "noble simplicity and calm grandeur" of antiquity were to be imitated, not copied. This important, if subtle, distinction was recognized by James Madison in his now famous *"Federalist"* number 14 in *The Federalist*: "Is it not the glory of the people of America that, whilst they have paid a decent regard to the opinions of former times and other nations, they have not suffered a blind veneration for antiquity...to overrule the suggestions of their good sense...and the lessons of their own experience." These practical politicians followed the popular maxim: "Reason the guide; classicism the adviser." Antiquity haunted the imagination of the founding fathers, who saw Greece in the age of Pericles and Augustan Rome as the noblest achievements of free men aspiring to govern themselves. In this conviction the first generation of the American republic called the upper chamber of its legislature the Senate, named the new building to house the new government a capitol (not a house of Parliament or a *hôtel de ville*), sculpted its heroes in togas, organized the Society of the Cincinnati, assigned Latin texts to the young, and sent them to study at college where the grounds were designated a campus. Soon political life was divided into Federalists and Republicans, terms springing from the Latin. And their arts took on a Platonic geometry, in which their architects and craftsmen discerned, as the poet Mark Akenside put it, "In matter's mouldering structures, the pure forms/Of Triangle or Circle, Cube or Cone."

Wendell Garrett

This royal throne of kings, this sceptered isle,
This earth of majesty, this seat of Mars,
This other Eden, demi-paradise,
This fortress built by Nature for herself
Against infection and the hand of war,
This happy breed of men, this little world,
This precious stone set in the silver sea,
Which serves it in the office of a wall,
Or as a moat defensive to a house,
Against the envy of less happier lands,
This blessed plot, this earth, this realm, this England....

William Shakespeare, *Richard II,* 1597

THE DYING John of Gaunt was apostrophizing the England of Elizabeth I, the virgin queen, whose achievement was to give her subjects the opportunity to cast their eyes westward and carve their place in the New World.

Richard Hakluyt claimed in his *Principall Navigations, Voyages and Discoveries of the English Nation* (1589–1600) that the English had "excelled all the nations and peoples of the earth" in "searching the most opposite corners and quarters of the world and...in compassing the vast globe."

In the eighteenth century, as disillusion grew about the much vaunted British model of secular salvation through parliamentary reform, a flood of writings extolled the glories of colonial America—a primitive country in the state of nature whose inhabitants were consumed with a passion for liberty and endowed by nature with all the attributes to realize the visions of the reforming *philosophes*. When the very existence of the new world in America was threatened by revolution, the liberals and revolutionaries of Europe militantly rallied to support the American colonists. They were fully conscious that they were fighting for their own liberties as much as for the liberties of peoples far across the sea.

The revolutionary strife in France differed enormously from the disruptive, but not violent, industrial revolution in England. It has long been generally held that the latter brought the old agricultural way of life in England to a close and established a new industrial civilization. But England is a small country and the center of an old society in which property and liberty have long been inseparable. The home of the individual Englishman has been his castle, and the ownership of land has been the greatest shield against despotism.

However, despite mass production and machine tools, doubled coal and iron production, and a great increase in cotton production, it has been persuasively argued that England remained a traditional society, horse-drawn and sail-driven, far into the nineteenth century. For most workers the unit of production was the workshop, still hierarchical and personal, paternal and fraternal. It followed the traditional pattern of a master employing only a few journeymen and working alongside them. The household remained the normal unit of production in farming, cottage industries, and crafts long after the advent of industrialism, and the agricultural revolution did not at once destroy communal values and rural sentiments long embedded in folk custom.

It is in England's small towns that both the continuities and changes in English social history have been most faithfully demonstrated. One of the most sympathetic and knowledgeable American observers to write about England was T. S. Eliot, who perceptively acknowledged that all history is unfinished history, and concluded: "So, while the light falls/On a winter's afternoon, in a secluded chapel/History is now and England."

Wendell Garrett

What is pure art according to the modern idea? It is the creation of an evocative magic, containing at once the object and the subject, the world external to the artist and the artist himself.

Charles Baudelaire, *Philosophic Art*, 1868

Charles Baudelaire (1821–1867), the eminent precursor of the French symbolists, is better known as a poet and essayist than as a critic of art. But in his aesthetic opinion, the good in art could only be achieved by conscious and imaginative effort: by striving after the ideal virtue or beauty, and constantly battling against the powerful, but senseless, impulses of Nature. The idea of copying Nature was to him as great a heresy as the idea of adding something extraneous, like "style," to Nature. Above all else, Baudelaire admired art that revealed the feelings and thoughts of the artistic personality; he opened a path for the new generation of poets and painters to symbolism, with its desire to attain the suggestiveness of music and its doctrine of the interpenetration of the senses.

Baudelaire recognized the brilliant logic for his own half-developed thoughts in Edgar Allan Poe's dictum in his 1844 *Marginalia* notes on Tennyson, "The orange ray of the spectrum and the buzz of the gnat...affect me with nearly similar sensations," which in turn led to Baudelaire's own theory on the mystic accord of the senses and symbols in his epoch-making sonnet, "Correspondances": "Les parfums, les couleurs, et les sons se répondent" (Scents, colors, and sounds interrelate).

In his own time, as today, Poe was the subject of critical disagreement: Tennyson thought him the most original genius, but Emerson pronounced him "the jingle man"; Whitman judged him "among the electric lights of imaginative literature, brilliant and dazzling, but with no heat," while both Howells and Twain found his method "mechanical." But Poe has always been considered a great poet in France, where his image of man's destiny as a frail boat out of control on the waters of life became a major symbol for the age.

The relevance of these complex developments lies in the extraordinary influence French symbolism had on American writers and artists in creating words and images that joined forces to direct individual minds to collective ideas, eventually constituting a whole—abstractly formulated ideals that assumed visible shapes. With the Revolution the figure of Columbia—symbolizing America—did not represent a geographical locale or a particular race, but a conglomeration of ideals and virtues, and she was recognized as such both at home and abroad. With independence the mighty American eagle, hatched in the midst of war and clutching arrows in one claw but an olive branch in the other, became the proud emblem of patriotism and the comforting symbol of unity and power. When the New York Mechanick Society desired a certificate of membership about 1785, it commissioned an engraver to weave together allegorical images of Liberty and Industry with a central arm-and-hammer motif and the inscription "By Hammer & Hand, all Arts do stand" to confirm the dignity of the mechanical arts in the free air of America. The American promise of abundance and plenty has been symbolized by the basket of fruit painted in still lifes (cover), the cornucopias carved on furniture, and the sheafs of wheat stamped on silver. "Their ancestors gave [Americans] the love of equality and of freedom," Alexis de Tocqueville observed, "but God Himself gave them the means of remaining equal and free by placing them upon a boundless continent."

An image, a symbol, an allegory—all can wield tremendous power: they can hold a nation together or break a culture apart. Standing for the mythic, invulnerable whole, an eagle, a star, a cross, or a fleur-de-lis has a special meaning for everyone who recognizes it. Rendered with realistic illusion and crystalline clarity, the still lifes of Severin Roesen are icons of the impact of abundance on American life, when as Whitman wrote, the United States was becoming "a teeming nation of nations."

History has a curious way of being circular. In 1908 T. S. Eliot discovered Arthur Symons's *Symbolist Movement in Literature*, which led him to the works of Charles Baudelaire. From Baudelaire he learned of "the possibility of fusion between the sordidly realistic and the phantasmagoric," of how the apparently common, emotional experiences of the modern city could be turned into materials for poetry, "to transmit [the poet's] personal and private agonies into something rich and strange, something universal and impersonal." Ironically Eliot's profound attraction to French symbolism and the work of Baudelaire was instrumental in bringing Poe, with his doctrine of decadence and his reaffirmation of evil, back to American letters.

Wendell Garrett

Cabinet-Makers, originally, were no more, than Spurious Indocile Chips; expelled by Joiners, for the Superfluity of their SAP. And who, by instilling stupid Notions, and Prejudice to Architecture, into the Minds of Youth educated under them; has been the Cause, that at this Time; 'tis a very great Difficulty to find one in Fifty of them; that can make a Book-Case.

Batty Langley, *The City and Countryman's Treasury of Design*, 1741

After the chaos of the Revolution, American skilled workmen, including cabinetmakers, were caught up in the transition to an industrial society. The gradual erosion of a paternalistic structure and its replacement by a system of wages for labor shifted many of the risks and some of the rewards from masters to journeymen. The stress of this transition often resulted in conflict as the American working class itself was continually altered in its composition after 1790 by infusions of rural farmers, European peasants, artisans, and casual day laborers, who brought with them undisciplined work habits, older ways, and antagonistic values.

It is not surprising to find what the English labor historian E. P. Thompson calls "alternate bouts of intense labour and of idleness wherever men were in control of their working lives." An English cabinetmaker who worked in New York City with seven others (two Americans, two Germans, and one man each from Ireland, England, and France) recalled in 1846 that "frequently...after several weeks of real hard work...a simultaneous cessation from work took place. As if...by tacit agreement, every hand" contributed "loose change," and an apprentice left the place and "speedily returned laden with wine, brandy, biscuits, and cheese." Songs came forth "from those who felt musical," and the same near ritual repeated itself two more times that day.

Some urban craftsmen adapted to change and shed the seasonal work habits of a family-oriented agricultural society to conform to the new imperatives. Others sought to extend and adapt older patterns of work, and still others challenged the masters by forming various journeymen associations. The General Society of Mechanics and Tradesmen was founded in New York City in 1785 by representatives of thirty-one different trades, and included among its members prominent craftsmen such as the cabinetmaker Duncan Phyfe. It found a place on its membership certificate for a picture of a plowman side by side with a house carpenter and a shipwright, all beneath the slogan "By Hammer and Hand all Arts do Stand."

In 1794, a year of political struggle and rapid price inflation, a massive procession of workingmen paraded by craft through the streets of New York in opposition to Federalist policies. An emerging "artisan republicanism" stressed individual ability and equality along with virtuous cooperation and a mutuality of interests against the landowners and moneyed men of the Federalist party. The turn to politics was not made in desperation, but in hope and confidence.

The journeymen cabinetmakers of New York City submitted a new book of prices to their employers in 1795, demanding to be "treated as men possessing an ingenious art." A few years later they walked out when the masters refused to honor an oral wage settlement. After the masters attempted to cut labor costs, a mass meeting of "the mechanics and manufacturers of New York City" in 1801 sent a memorial to Congress beseeching the "protecting hand of government."

For a brief period following the Republican triumph of 1800, the "yeomanry of the city," as Thomas Jefferson called them, could claim that they were heirs to the "spirit of '76." The town meetings, the popular political societies, and the symbolism of Fourth of July celebrations of the "revolution of 1800" were indeed the consummation of the Revolution of 1776. As the Jeffersonian movement transmuted eighteenth-century republicanism into nineteenth-century democracy, the artisan republicanism of urban craftsmen remained a legacy for the future.

Wendell Garrett

ANTIQUES

Antiquities are history defaced, or some remnants of history which casually escaped the shipwreck of time.

Francis Bacon, *The Advancement of Learning,* 1605

In Shakespeare's time, England became conscious of itself as a unique political entity—an empire. By the time of the Hanoverians the success of this vigorous nation in restraining kings and instituting responsible government made it the center of attention everywhere. The harvest was still the barometer of the economy, loyalties were parochial, and privilege and hierarchy were not questioned. It was a rural land of hamlets and villages, but life was not idyllic behind the plaster and thatch of the hovels of the poor—ramshackle warrens of filth, squalor, and disease. Firmly controlled by tradition, these peasants farmed as their forebears had farmed for centuries. However, an incessant demand for wool and a government bounty on corn resulted in big profits and made the possession of great estates a highly desirable form of investment.

By prudent marriages and careful purchases of their native heath some of the great lords and country gentlemen amassed large holdings on which they built rural palaces of enormous size and grandeur. The country house was not only a social center, a repository of tradition, and the nursery of the family, but also the gathering place where governments were made and unmade, and alliances planned and executed. In the last half of the eighteenth century many a young man was sent off on a grand tour of the Continent to bring back the spoils of the Renaissance and the classical world to furnish these grand houses. At the same time, exotic trees and plants from foreign lands were assimilated into the English garden.

In this era life was lived in costume. From the king on his throne to the bishop in his lawn, the judge in his ermine, the soldier in his scarlet, and the laborer in his smock frock, each dressed his part and was expected to act in character. It was England's Augustan age, when the languages and images of the ancient Mediterranean cultures came easily to people of education. In 1769, for example, when Josiah Wedgwood expanded his pottery works at Burslem, he naturally enough christened it Etruria and boasted that he would throw pots in Staffordshire at least as handsome as those of the Etruscans.

There was a fundamental strength and resilience to the social hierarchy of the Georgian landed gentry, whose domination was consolidated early in the eighteenth century and never seriously challenged. Stability could be maintained despite pockets of disorder because the economy worked well enough to profit the rich, keep practically everyone else alive, and promise improvement for all. Above all, England was successful in war, conquest, and colonization.

When George III died in 1820 he left behind a country twice as populous and vastly richer than it had been when he assumed the throne sixty years earlier. On the threshold of the nineteenth century, England was the foremost capitalist society in Europe and the one most resistant to pressure for violent change.

Wendell Garrett

[Washington] is sometimes called the City of Magnificent Distances, but it might with greater propriety be termed the City of Magnificent Intentions; for it is only on taking a bird's-eye view of it from the top of the Capitol that one can at all comprehend the vast designs of its projector....

Charles Dickens, *American Notes: A Journey,* 1842

Pierre Charles L'Enfant's plan for a Federal district, like the constitutional plan for a Federal government, remained for several decades only a statement of "Magnificent Intentions." The American people tended to ignore their central government, and the politicians, reflecting this mood of localism, tended to avoid any aggrandizement of their central enclave. Until 1834 there were only two major Federal buildings (and four minor ones) in the capital city—the Capitol and the White House (see cover). Between their hilltop sites was a squalid landscape of marshes, barren knolls, and shabby houses. Where majestic avenues were to sweep, rough quarried stones marked projected intersections; where monuments had been planned, tree stumps stood and rubbish heaps accumulated. Visitors from the cultivated capitals of Europe and from the settled splendors of New York City, Boston, and Philadelphia scoffed at the pretensions of this undeveloped wilderness. The uncompleted character of the capital city reflected that of the nation.

In his scheme for Washington L'Enfant intended to embody the main principles of the Constitution. To express the constitutional separation of powers, for example, the Capitol, the White House, and the Supreme Court (which waited, in fact, until 1935 for its own building) were to be separated by considerable distances, and situated to command different aspects. The streets were to radiate in all directions, a symbolic invitation to citizens to come and be heard. The plan was inconclusive about where the administrative departments were to be housed, but then so was the Constitution.

What underlay these arrangements was the cultural ambivalence toward centralized political authority that existed in extreme form throughout the nation during this period. Jeffersonian America revered the Constitution but feared the potential for tyranny it saw lurking in the government the Constitution had created. Madison summed it up when he wrote in *The Federalist* Number 47 that "The accumulation of all powers legislative, executive and judiciary in the same hands...may justly be pronounced the very definition of tyranny."

To the extent that the constitutional theme of L'Enfant's city plan came to life in this period, it was in caricature: not just separate districts but separate and self-sustaining communities formed around the two elected branches, separated from each other by the mile-wide wilderness of thickets and virtually uninhabited moors that made travel between the presidential and congressional sectors treacherous at best, and nearly impossible during the rainy season. Living and working under such dreadful conditions, it is not surprising that most congressmen, deprived of a sense of permanence, came to despise Washington as a physically isolated small town: an average of one- to two-thirds left Congress every two years, many by resignation.

Was our national government in the Jeffersonian era a failure? Consider the assemblage of people who occupied the White House: Jefferson, Madison, Monroe, and Adams. Daniel Webster, Henry Clay, and John C. Calhoun, three of the greatest senators in history, made their mark in this period. John Marshall was chief justice of the Supreme Court, and Samuel Chase and Joseph Story were among those who served as associate justices. Talented people do not always create good government, but in the Jeffersonian era, they did. The early American state fought wars, secured new territories, built roads and waterways, carried on relations with other governments, and aided economic development. More important than even these accomplishments, the Federal City—the company town of the national government—kept the nation and its new government alive and intact. And having secured a nation, this generation bent their energies on securing a continent.

Wendell Garrett

Our countrymen are about to abandon the good old, grave, solid manners of Englishmen, their ancestors, and adopt all the apery, levity, and frivolity, of the French.

John Adams to Abigail Adams, January 31, 1793

The American colonies began as an extension of medieval Europe—villages with common lands, a religious center for the city-state, handcraft industries, and, in the southern colonies, a social complex of liege lords, patentees, vast estates, indentured servants and slaves, and a system of primogeniture and entail. As they grew, America's coastal towns continued to look to Europe: their citizens imported their learning, books, ideas, and their social systems; they went to Europe for relief from the tedium of colonial life, for intellectual stimulation, and for mercantile supplies; and thither, if they could, they sent their children to be educated.

Next to Protestant England, the country that had the longest and most important impact in America was Latin and Catholic France. Not only did Americans go to France, but thousands of Frenchmen visited the New World—explorers, Huguenots, refugees, scientists, artists, visionaries, propagandists, noblemen, and commoners. They found here a refuge from persecution, opportunities for building a new life, a laboratory for social study, a field for exploration, and an ally (or an enemy) in politics and war. The dynamic relationship forged between these sister republics goes a long way in explaining the fascination of Americans with France.

While this relationship was not static, certain elements have remained the same. The French have always possessed intellectual prestige; the connections between American learned societies and French savants have been remarkably intimate, especially given the linguistic and geographical obstacles. Representative institutions in America owe much to Rousseau, and the writings of Montesquieu played an important part in shaping the Constitution. In addition, earlier even than John Adams, Montesquieu made the democratic observation that trial by jury gave the people a share in the execution of the laws.

In the eighteenth century, French became the preeminent international language, supplanting even Latin. A reading knowledge of French was not uncommon among genteel American colonists from the earliest times. In the eighteenth century, also, French manners conquered the world, representing a kind of art to Americans. Adams, in Paris in 1778, was impressed by French conduct: "The delights of France are innumerable. The politeness, the elegance, the softness, the delicacy, are extreme. In short, stern and haughty republican as I am, I cannot help loving these people for their earnest desire and assiduity to please."

At the beginning of the nineteenth century, the *salon* spirit was abroad in the new nation: dancing, formal dinners, and the frivolous creations of Parisian milliners and dressmakers dominated fashionable society. Cooking has always had its place among the French arts: Thomas Jefferson brought back from Paris a fastidious taste for French wines and food, along with a French chef for the White House (although Patrick Henry denounced him for abjuring "his native victuals"). During James Monroe's presidency, Baron Jean Guillaume Hyde de Neuville used to puzzle and astound plain-living Yankees at his dinners by serving them boneless turkey, puddings in the shape of fowl, and fresh cod disguised as a salad. In the fine arts, the great French sculptor Jean Antoine Houdon executed portrait busts of the founding fathers, and the French portraitist Charles B. J. F. de Saint-Memin took likenesses in all our principal cities between 1793 and 1815. In architecture, the ardently Francophile Livingston clan of upstate New York employed French architects, while Sir Charles Lyell, traveling along the Mississippi River in the 1840's, found many elegant French-style mansions and gardens.

At the end of the nineteenth century, Germany began to exert increasing influence on American thought. But no Continental nation ever surpassed the impact of France on American manners and fashions, aesthetics, and political theory.

Wendell Garrett

The history of the Victorian Age will never be written: we know too much about it.

Lytton Strachey, *Eminent Victorians*, 1918

The Victorian age exhibited all the diversity, and much of the perversity, of which the human mind is capable. It was an age that enthralled some and appalled others; an age of severe manners and morals and of considerable latitude in behavior, when the underworld of pornography became more obtrusive and prudery more obsessive. It has been described by historians variously as an age of equipoise, reform, and conservative revolution.

When Queen Victoria died in 1901, sixty-four years after coming to the throne, the *Annual Register* remarked that the national feeling of forlornness was unparalleled since the death of King Alfred. The men and women of the new century, for all their pride in the present, had an ineradicable homesickness for the past. The coming of the railway was the great watershed, and Victorians like William Makepeace Thackeray felt they had lived in two distinct worlds: "It was only yesterday; but what a gulf between now and then! *Then* was the old world. Stage-coaches...riding-horses, pack-horses, highway-men, knights in armour, Norman invaders, Roman legions, Druids....We are of the age of steam."

The Victorians' sense of history was a bundle of often paradoxical ideas and attitudes, based on myth as much as fact. According to "the theory of the Norman yoke," before 1066 the Anglo-Saxons had lived as free and equal citizens and had governed themselves with representative institutions. The theory was used by radicals in their attacks on landed and aristocratic power, the system of primogeniture, and the game laws. The Victorians also used the past, particularly a deeply embedded medievalism, to highlight what they felt were the failings of the secular, industrial present. When they put up a new building of any importance they made it look old from the start. Even the Crystal Palace, that monument to modernity, had a "medieval court" full of stained glass and encaustic tiles. Symptomatic of the sentimental fancy of the age was the vogue for building ruins of nonexistent castles and follies on country estates, and for Sir Walter Scott's novels, with their nostalgia for the age of chivalry.

The more pressing reason for this recurrence of glamorized medievalism was the wish to discover a society more stable and equitable, an intellectual temper more unified and free of anxiety, than their own age was capable of. The faster the rate of change, the more the Victorians longed for a fixed order. They lived their everyday lives according to two times: the old leisurely one and the new headlong one. They were, in a particularly prominent way, at the crossroads between the traditional and the new, demonstrating for us, their heirs, the twin forces of continuity and change that are always at work in society.

If the Victorians had been the fools and buffoons their successors thought they were, grossly incompetent in thought and action, their society would have collapsed in chaos. If, on the other hand, their leading figures had been the towering giants of wisdom some of their contemporaries took them to be, they would not have bequeathed the twentieth century quite so daunting a heritage of unsolved problems. Theirs was an orderly and well-defined society, but not an inherently stable one. Faced as they were by an experience for which nothing in the history of mankind had prepared them, they did their best, in various ways and according to their various lights, to leave us a more stable, better world. Notwithstanding the buffeting of change, they maintained what Carlyle called, in "Signs of the Times," "a faith in the imperishable dignity of man; in the high vocation of which, throughout this his earthly history, he has been appointed."

Wendell Garrett

Regionalism in early American tea tables

BY ALBERT SACK

THE UNITED STATES was, by its Constitution, both a nation and a collection of regions. The differences, not only between the Colonies but also between the separate regions, were recognized even in the eighteenth century. Benjamin Franklin pointed out that each colony had "peculiar expressions, familiar to its own people, but strange and unintelligible to others."[1] The long Atlantic coastal plain, with its multitude of rivers and swamps, tended to keep Americans apart. Roads were scarce and, except for the coastal urban centers, the population was scattered thinly on farms along the seaboard. By the end of the eighteenth century most Americans recognized the existence of distinct groupings of states: a central "middle" group; a "Northern," or New England, group; a Southern bloc; and occasionally "coastal" and "back country" regions. Jedidiah Morse's *American Geography* of 1793 listed the "grand Division of the United States" as Northern, Middle, and Southern, and in 1819 added the "Western States and Territories."[2] Within these major divisions there were widely accepted subdivisions: the two poles of New England (Portsmouth, New Hampshire, and New Haven, Connecticut); Massachusetts's North Shore and the Connecticut River valley; upstate and metropolitan New York; urban Philadelphia and western Pennsylvania; the Chesapeake Bay tobacco country and the rice culture of the Carolina low country. American society exhibited tremendous regional diversity and fierce sectional loyalties, rooted deeply in colonial culture, tradition, economics, and government. Early American furniture displays marked regional differences and local preferences that were fundamental—a tangled skein of diversities of form, materials, construction, and decoration by which it is now possible to identify and attribute the handiwork of craftsmen working within regional schools of cabinetmaking.

This colorful variety in American cultural life, and particularly these regional differences in American furniture—as complex and ambiguous as they are—somehow are bound up and unified into a national style that we can identify as uniquely American. The New World was different from the Old; America was not England. And the rich diversity of American culture, of which furniture is but one expression, can only be understood in the context of our pluralistic society—a society of multiple allegiances, mixed loyalties, divergent economies, different religions, and other interests which held the individual citizen in a sort of loose societal orbit.

My father, Israel Sack (1883–1959), began his career as an antiques dealer in Boston in 1905 and quickly grasped the unique quality of American furniture. Someone once asked him how he was able to differentiate between American and English antique furniture: "That's easy," he said, "by its accent!" During the first decade of this century, long before museum collections were formed and American furniture was studied seriously, some collectors and a few dealers began to sort out the differences not only between American and English furniture but also between American furniture of different regions.

By now we can be proud of our accomplishments in the study of our furniture history. In fact it is widely recognized that we are further advanced and more sophisticated in regional identifications than English furniture historians who, until recently and with several notable exceptions, have tended to con-

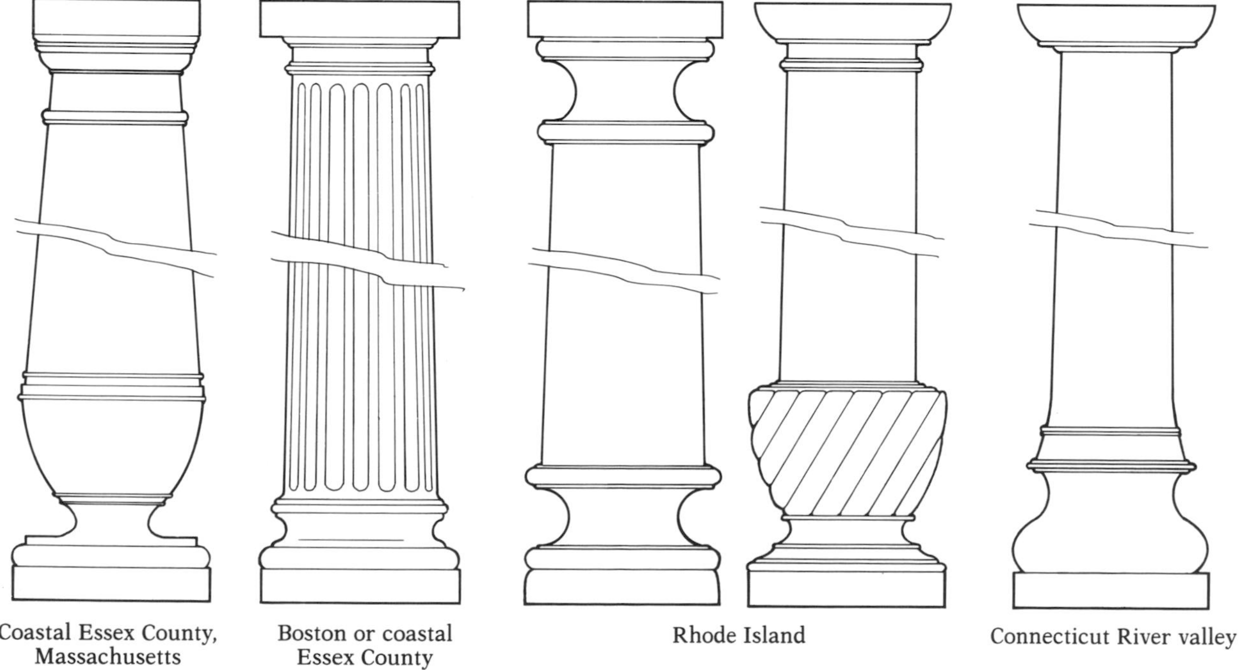

Coastal Essex County, Massachusetts — Boston or coastal Essex County — Rhode Island — Connecticut River valley

centrate on furniture made in London. The earliest published recognition of regionalism in American furniture is contained in two seminal works by Luke Vincent Lockwood, *English Furniture* (1909) and *Colonial Furniture in America* (1913). Lockwood recognized the Americanness of pieces of furniture that he had earlier attributed to England because of their sophistication. However, in the catalogue to the great loan exhibition of American furniture and other decorative arts at the Metropolitan Museum in Art in 1909 during the Hudson-Fulton celebration, the only regional identifications were a Philadelphia high chest of drawers and matching dressing table, a desk-and-bookcase with blocking and shells described as "presumably made by a cabinetmaker in Newport," and rather incredibly for this early date, a dozen pieces captioned "Furniture made by Duncan Phyfe."[3]

The founding of *The Magazine* ANTIQUES in 1922 under its truly great editor, Homer Eaton Keyes, and the opening of the American Wing of the Metropolitan Museum of Art in 1924 spurred interest in the regional centers of American cabinetmaking. During its first two years ANTIQUES published articles about John Goddard, Duncan Phyfe, and William Savery, which opened a discussion of regionalism and resulted in the attribution of most Rhode Island and Boston block-front furniture to Goddard, most New York Federal tables and chairs to Phyfe, and most Philadelphia Chippendale furniture to Savery.

Times have changed. Careful research into the details of design, construction, and secondary woods has led to the identification of forms and characteristics distinctive of specific centers, among them Portsmouth, Salem, Boston, Rhode Island, New York, the Connecticut River valley, Philadelphia, Maryland, and Charleston. In addition, detailed studies of signed and documented pieces from these centers have not only helped scholars attribute unsigned works to these craftsmen but also refine their understanding of the products produced by each center. The imaginative and vigorous work being carried on by the Colonial Williamsburg Foundation in Williamsburg, Virginia, and the Museum of Early Southern Decorative Arts in Winston-Salem, North Carolina, is expanding our knowledge of the furniture of the South.

Undeniably, the study of American furniture history is healthy and mature today. But to me it is still an exciting experience to look inside the drawer of a pristine little dressing table and find a faded family label that reads "a relic from England" and to be able with certainty to state that it was made by an anonymous but obviously highly skilled artist-craftsman in or around Salem, Massachusetts.

This article on regionalism in American furniture focuses on tea tables because they enjoyed such widespread popularity in the eighteenth century, when the custom of drinking tea was a new mark of luxury and leisure. Compared with other forms, the tea table appears to have been made in prolific numbers in a wide variety of styles in nearly all the cabinetmaking centers.

I should like to add a note of caution: all the broad generalizations made here are subject to the exceptions and inconsistencies that force us to be cautious about making firm attributions. True scholarship is an evolution: today's truisms are inevitably subject to tomorrow's revisions.

ALBERT SACK is a partner in the firm of Israel Sack, Incorporated. He is also the author of *Fine Points of Furniture, Early American* (New York, 1950).

New York Philadelphia Maryland Charleston

Regional characteristics in tea tables, from North to South

Portsmouth, New Hampshire

Six rectangular tea tables of the kind shown in Plate I have survived. On the basis of family histories, they have all been attributed to Portsmouth, although the possibility of a Boston origin should not be ruled out.[4] The legs are braced by arched, double C-scroll, crossed (saltire) stretchers surmounted by a pierced finial. The outer surface of the legs is molded and the inner edge is chamfered. The skirt is covered with crossbanded veneer.

In contrast to this highly sophisticated form is a circular, tray-top, swing-leg tea table of cherry and birch in the Museum of Fine Arts, Boston, that is also attributed to New Hampshire, possibly Portsmouth.[5] The thin cabriole legs have pointed knees and pad feet.

Pl. I. Tea table, Portsmouth, New Hampshire, 1765–1775. Mahogany and mahogany veneer, and maple; height 27⅛, width 35, depth 23 inches. *Metropolitan Museum of Art.*

Fig. 1. Tilt-top tea table, coastal Essex County, Massachusetts, 1760–1780. Mahogany; height 29¼, width of top 37 inches. *Private collection; photograph by courtesy of Israel Sack, Incorporated.*

Fig. 2. Tilt-top tea table, coastal Essex County, 1760–1780. Mahogany; height 28, diameter of top 33⅞ inches. *Private collection; Sack photograph.*

Coastal Essex County, Massachusetts

Rectangular tea tables on four fixed legs are more prevalent in New England than round, tilt-top tripod-base tea tables. In coastal Essex County the cabriole legs on rectangular tea tables tend to have high knees, long slender ankles, and either crisp pad feet resting on a platform or claw-and-ball feet. Early Queen Anne tea tables from coastal Essex County tend to have a top board with a broad overhang; later the top usually has an applied tray molding and is more integrated with the skirt. These rectangular tea tables, which are less common in New York and Philadelphia, combine straight and curved lines in their design in a harmonious way that epitomizes the understated elegance characteristic of coastal Massachusetts furniture.

The tilt-top tables made during the Chippendale period in coastal Essex County illustrated in Figures 1 and 2 are both typical in many ways and atypical in others from pieces identified with the region.[6] Each has a plain, tapering pillar (although fluted pillars are found on some Essex County tables) terminating in one case in a plain, flattened urn and in the other in a spiral fluted urn. The serpentine-edged rectangular top was second in popularity to the circular top. But the piecrust top, so popular in Philadelphia, is rare on Massachusetts tables. The tops tilt on a block, usually of birch or maple; the cleats are generally birch, maple, or mahogany. The cabriole legs are either plain or richly carved with acanthus sprays, sometimes both above and below a central panel or cartouche on the knee. The legs of the table shown in Figure 2 are decorated with the star punch, or "snowflake," found on Salem furniture. The underside of the legs and the base of the pillar have notched or scalloped edges with a spur often found on coastal Massachusetts tea tables. The attenuated claw-and-ball feet have well-defined, birdlike talons.

Boston, Massachusetts

Rectangular Boston tea tables with fixed cabriole legs have a distinctive tray top with a molded lip, sometimes notched or indented corners, a boldly scalloped skirt in a series of ogee curves (sometimes with a candle slide in each end rail), and gracefully curved legs on crisp, wafer pad feet (Fig. 3). Eastern Massachusetts cabriole legs in the Queen Anne period generally have an unadorned high knee, a long slender ankle, and a pad foot resting on a platform or wafer. The convex scalloped apron is nailed and glued to the rail and a thin bead is sometimes applied just above it. When the corners of the moldings of the tray top are indented they are separate pieces. Two tea tables in the collection of the Society for the Preservation of New England Antiquities in Boston are similar to that illustrated in Figure 3:[7] one has the applied skirt and the other, more usual, variant has a scalloped rail forming the skirt. Neither has candle slides. These exquisite tables, free of all ornament, are masterpieces of colonial craftsmanship.

The six known so-called turret-top, or buttress, tea tables (see Pl. II), with applied, half-round projections for teacups, are unique to Boston. In the example shown here the straightish cabriole legs with deep knee brackets have carved knees and the claw-and-ball feet have knuckled claws. The rarity and distinctive quality of these six tables as well as the differences between them have been thoroughly documented.[8]

Fig. 3. Tea table, Boston, 1750–1770.
Mahogany; height 27, width 29, depth 19 inches.
Collection of Peter W. Eliot; Sack photograph.

Pl. II. Turret-top tea table, Boston, 1750–1770.
Mahogany; height 27½, width 30, depth 19⅜ inches.
Museum of Fine Arts, Boston, M. and M. Karolik Collection.

Newport, Rhode Island

Newport furniture is distinguished by superb craftsmanship, dense, richly colored mahogany, and clean lines. Shared New England characteristics in the splendid marble-tray-top table illustrated in Plate III make it possible to attribute it to either Boston or Newport. The dished top, indented corners, and high-kneed cabriole legs are found on both eastern Massachusetts and Newport tea tables, as is the perfect visual balance between the sides and the legs. However, the solidity of the table and the way the dish rim of the top is hewn from the solid makes me feel that this table originated in Newport. (When Joseph

Pl. III. Tea table, New England, 1735–1745. Mahogany with marble top; height 27⅛, width 28¾, depth 16⅝ inches. *Henry Francis du Pont Winterthur Museum, Winterthur, Delaware.*

Downs published it in 1952 he assigned the table to New York City.[9]) In any event, if a single piece of American Queen Anne furniture were to be selected to compete with the chef-d'oeuvre of eighteenth-century cabinetwork in England or France, this tea table would be my first choice.

Tables with rounded corners shaped like porringer basins are widely known as porringer-top tables and were used for a variety of purposes. They are traditionally attributed to Rhode Island (see Fig. 4), but there is reasonable evidence to suggest that they were also made in eastern Massachusetts and southeastern Connecticut. The majority of the tables have straight skirts that are shaped only at the junction with the legs; a few have boldly scalloped aprons. The tops of these tables are secured to the frames in various ways: by glued blocks, by pins through the top, and by maple blocks mortised into the sides and nailed to the underside of the top. Most have straight, turned, tapering legs and wafer pad feet. The diminutive size, boldly scrolled skirt, and slightly flared stance of the legs of the example illustrated place it in the class of a masterpiece. The more characteristic or standard tables were made of maple and walnut as well as mahogany.

Characteristic of Newport is the rectangular tray-top table on cabriole legs that are square in section from knee to ankle and terminate in thin, pointed slipper feet (see Fig. 5). The severe, straight skirt has an applied quarter-round molding. A relatively large number of these tables survive and most are remarkably consistent in design and construction.[10] On these Newport tea tables the top is rabbeted to fit into the skirt well, and the tray molding, which is rounded on the outside and has a broad convex inner edge, is nailed to the top. The quarter-round apron moldings nailed to the bottom of the skirts are completed by shaped, segmented brackets glued to the inside of the knees. The visual success of these delicate, graceful tables can be attributed to the unbroken line of their squared cabriole legs. A variant has a cabriole leg with a carved ring separating the upper leg, which is octagonal in section, from the lower leg, which is round and terminates in a slipper foot (see Fig. 6). In the example illustrated the convex apron has a central pendant and ogee-shaped knee returns; the applied tray molding is coved.

In the tour de force of Newport tray-top tea tables of the Chippendale period the ogee curves of the top are repeated in the apron, somewhat in the manner of the blocking found on Newport case pieces (see Pl. V). Six examples of this form are known, the most famous of which is documented as having been made by John Goddard for Jabez Bowen in 1763.[11] The example illustrated here is the most recent of the group to surface, and because of its construction and carving has been attributed by Michael Moses to John Townsend.[12] The sides of the frame are carved from the solid, not applied. The ogee-shaped tray moldings which follow the configuration of the frame are also carved from the solid. The top is attached to the frame with blocks glued to the underside and mortised braces. The knife-edged cabriole legs, square in section, are intaglio-carved at the knee with a palmette-and-leaf motif. The legs terminate in open-taloned, claw-and-ball feet.

Fig. 4. Porringer-top tea table, Newport, Rhode Island, 1760–1770. Mahogany; height 25, width 22¼, depth 17¾ inches. *Private collection; photograph by Helga Photo Studio.*

Pl. IV. Tea table, Newport, 1750–1770. Maple; height 27¼, width 20, depth 30½ inches. *Private collection; Sack photograph.*

Fig. 5. Tea table, Newport, 1740–1770. Mahogany; height 26, width 31, depth 19 inches. *Private collection; Sack photograph.*

Fig. 6. Tea table, Newport, 1740–1770. Mahogany; height 26, width 30⅞, depth 18¾ inches. *Art Institute of Chicago.*

Pl. V. Tea table attributed to John Townsend (1732–1809), Newport, 1755–1765. Mahogany and yellow poplar; height 27⅝, width 34, depth 21⅛ inches. *Collection of Mr. and Mrs. George M. Kaufman; photograph by Dirk Bakker.*

Consistent with the handsome designs developed by Newport craftsmen is a rare straight-legged table in the Chinese Chippendale style which has pierced cross stretchers and an applied tray frame with an ornately scrolled openwork gallery (Fig. 7). The four Marlborough legs are stop-fluted on the outside faces and chamfered on the inside. Some of the motifs—stop-fluting, cross-hatching on the rails, rope carving, and fretwork brackets—were also used by Newport cabinetmakers on pembroke, or breakfast, tables and on card tables.[13]

Round, tilt-top Chippendale tea tables from Rhode Island differ from those from Massachusetts most notably in the pillar: Rhode Island balusters with an urn tend to have a more fully developed urn; those without an urn have straight, columnar shafts, plain in most cases and stop-fluted in a few.[14] The rounded feet tend to be more blunt than those from Massachusetts, and a few, attributed to John Goddard, have carved, five-toed paws. The rims of the trays on Rhode Island examples have a smooth inner outline and are deeper than those on Massachusetts tables.

Fig. 7. Tea table, Newport, 1760–1780. Mahogany and chestnut; height 27¼, width 34½, depth 21 inches. *Winterthur Museum.*

Connecticut River valley

Tilt-top tea tables from the Hartford region reflect a strong Philadelphia influence, particularly those attributed to Eliphalet Chapin (Fig. 8). The Philadelphia features are the flattened ball-and-ring turnings of the tapered pedestal, the long cylindrical pillar, and the use of a bird-cage attachment. The use of local cherry as the primary wood and the beautifully shaped serpentine top beveled on the underside are characteristic of Hartford tilt-top tables.[15] A painted tea table, probably made there, with an octagonal top supported by an urn and flared pillar, and with thin legs terminating in elongated pad feet, is in the American Wing of the Metropolitan Museum of Art.[16]

Connecticut River valley rectangular Queen Anne tea tables, also made of cherry, tend to have a broad tray molding around the top, delicate cabriole legs which terminate in small raised pads, and a scalloped skirt (see Fig. 9). The boldly scalloped skirt on the table in Figure 10 makes it an outstanding example of the form. Historic Deerfield, in Deerfield, Massachusetts, has a group of these tables in its collection.[17]

Fig. 8. Tilt-top tea table attributed to Eliphalet Chapin (1741–1807), East Windsor, Connecticut, 1770–1790. Cherry; height 28, width of top, 45 inches. *Private collection; Sack photograph.*

Fig. 9. Tea table, Connecticut River Valley, 1750–1780. Cherry; height 26½, width 28½, depth 19½ inches. *Private collection; Sack photograph.*

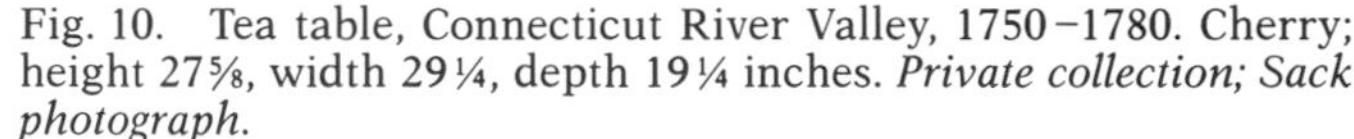

Fig. 10. Tea table, Connecticut River Valley, 1750–1780. Cherry; height 27⅝, width 29¼, depth 19¼ inches. *Private collection; Sack photograph.*

Pl. VI. Tea table, New York City, 1760–1770. Mahogany; height 27¼, length 34½, depth 21 inches. *Sack photograph.*

Fig. 11. Tilt-top tea table, New York City, 1760–1770. Mahogany; height 29, diameter of top 31 inches. *Private collection; Sack photograph.*

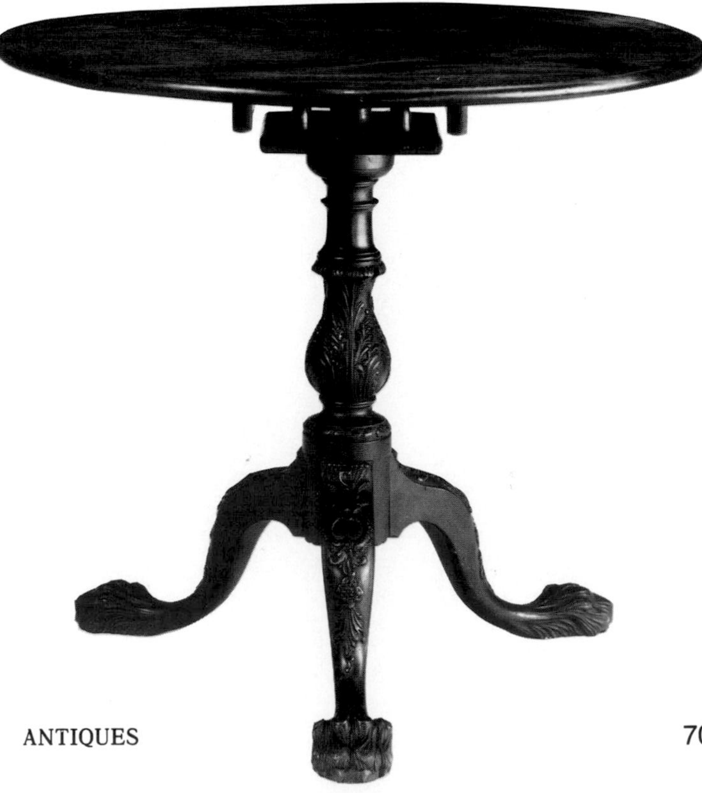

New York City

Rectangular tea tables made in New York City during the Chippendale period are much rarer than the circular, tilt-top variety (see Fig. 11). Most of the known examples have a gadrooned skirt and richly carved knees (Pl. VI). One in the Metropolitan Museum of Art has straight skirt rails and plain knees.[18] The group shares the distinctive New York regional characteristic of blocklike claw-and-ball feet with angular knuckles.

The cup-and-flared-shaft pillar is one of the classic features of New York tea tables with round, rimless tops.[19] These pillars are supported by cabriole legs, with or without acanthus-leaf carving on the knees, that terminate in blocklike claw-and-ball feet.

Pl. VII. Tilt-top tea table, Philadelphia, 1760–1780. Mahogany; height 27½, diameter of top 32⅞ inches. *Collection of Mr. and Mrs. E. G. Nicholson; photograph by courtesy of Christie's.*

Philadelphia

Round, tilt-top Chippendale tables with a turned pillar and tripod base were particularly popular in Philadelphia (see Pl. VII and Figs. 12, 13) Characteristic Philadelphia features are the molded rim carved from the solid around the top on some examples, the piecrust edge, also cut from the solid, on others; the bird cage; the baluster consisting of a flattened ball surmounted by a tapering column on some, a fluted column rising from a carved ball on others; the bold thrust of the cabriole legs with either plain knees or knees carved with a broad acanthus leaf; and bold claw-and-ball feet with powerful talons. The cleats under the tilt tops are rounded on the bottom and taper toward both ends. The bird-cage boxes permit the top both to tilt into a vertical position and to rotate. (The bird cages on American examples are taller than those on English ones, and the uprights are baluster shaped rather than cylindrical.) Philadelphia cabinetmakers generally used finely figured boards of mahogany for the tops of these tables and embellished the bases with the crisp carving which gives Philadelphia furniture its classic urbanity.

A singular feature of Philadelphia round tilt-top tea tables is the strong lift and tight arch of the thin,

Fig. 12. Tilt-top tea table, Philadelphia, 1760–1780.
Walnut; height 28¼, diameter of top 35½ inches.
Private collection; Sack photograph.

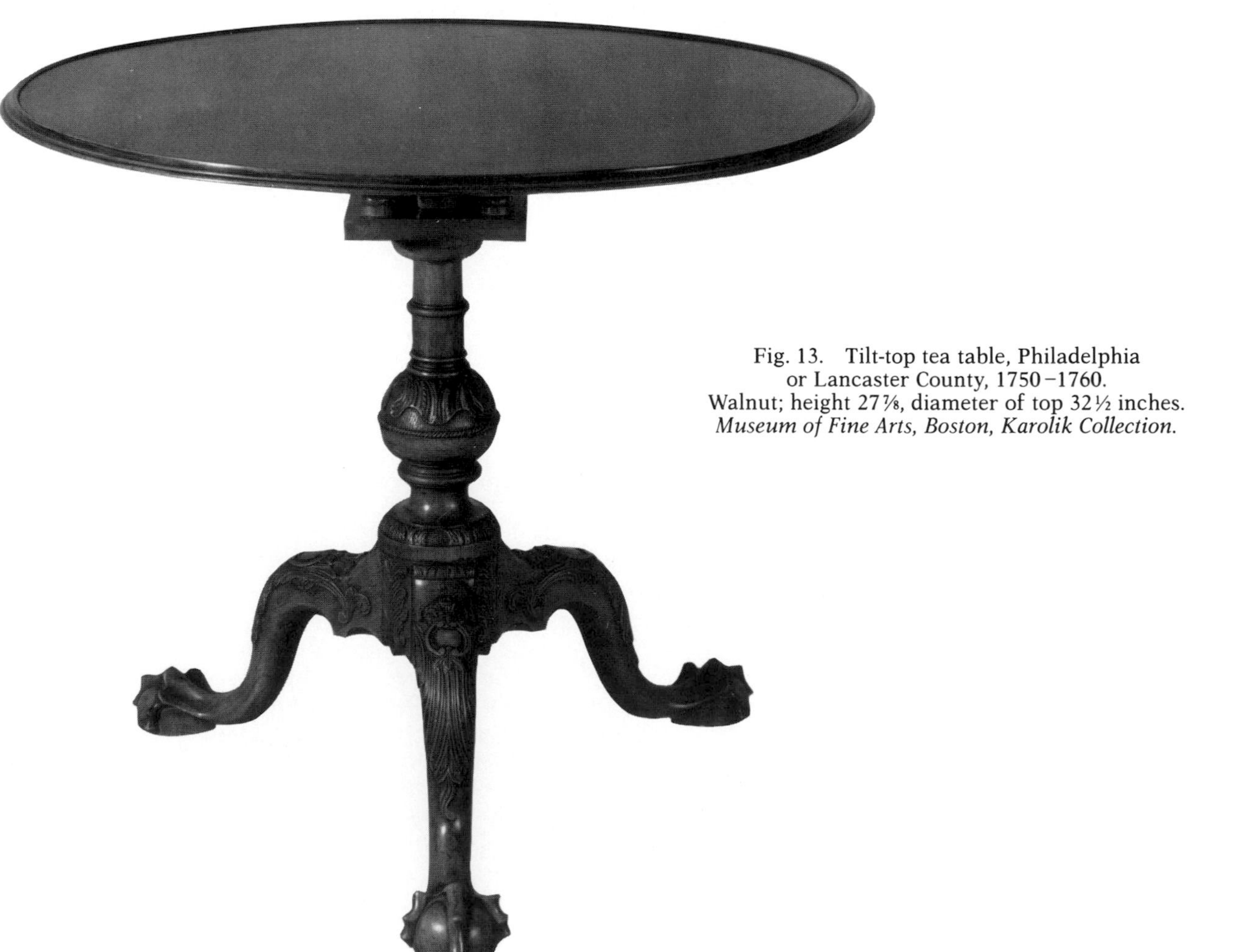

Fig. 13. Tilt-top tea table, Philadelphia
or Lancaster County, 1750–1760.
Walnut; height 27⅞, diameter of top 32½ inches.
Museum of Fine Arts, Boston, Karolik Collection.

tense ankle on the legs that give these tables a vertical emphasis. Some examples have pad feet resting on platforms while others have claw-and-ball feet in which the finely sculptured claws appear to grip the ball particularly tightly. Some versions have richly carved tops, pillars, and knees, while others are basically plain, reflecting the preference of the client more than the skill of the craftsman or the date of a particular piece.[20]

The rectangular tray-top tea table popular in New England is a rare form in Philadelphia (see Fig. 14). I know of fewer than one dozen surviving examples of high quality, carved or uncarved. Crisp, rich carving on the bold convex apron, similar carving on the knees of the cabriole legs which gracefully taper into long ankles, and claw-and-ball feet of the kind found on Philadelphia tilt-top tea tables are all regional characteristics of rectangular Philadelphia tea tables.

Maryland

Round tilt-top tea tables from Maryland share many features with their Philadelphia counterparts, although these features tend to be somewhat exaggerated: a heavier baluster with an urn or a ball and rings, and unusually long acanthus leaf carving on the knees. One surviving Maryland Queen Anne tea table has a square top;[21] another, from the Chippendale period, has a piecrust top (Fig. 15).

Charleston, South Carolina

The early work of E. Milby Burton, and more recently that of Frank L. Horton and his staff at the Museum of Early Southern Decorative Arts (MESDA) in Winston-Salem, North Carolina, have shed new light on Southern furniture in general and Charleston cabi-

Fig. 14. Tea table attributed to Benjamin Randolph (1721–1791) with carving attributed to Hercules Courtenay (1744?–1784), Philadelphia, 1774. Mahogany, cherry, and pine; height 29½, width 25¾, depth 17½ inches. *Philadelphia Museum of Art, gift of H. Richard Dietrich Jr.*

Fig. 15. Tilt-top tea table, Maryland, 1760–1770. Mahogany; height 28½, diameter of top 34¾ inches. *Private collection; photograph by courtesy of the Baltimore Museum of Art.*

network in particular. Burton documented the making of Chippendale piecrust tea tables in Charleston, but since research on these identifications was still so embryonic he suggested that because Charleston cabinetmakers followed English prototypes so closely some tea tables attributed to English makers may in fact have been made in Charleston.[22] The York, Pennsylvania, antiques dealer Joe Kindig Jr. once observed that piecrust tables from the South have shorter scallops on the rim than their Philadelphia counterparts.[23] As early as 1740 an "expatriated" Philadelphia cabinetmaker was in Charleston and advertised that he made "all sorts of Tea Tables."[24]

The curators at MESDA attribute the table illustrated in Figure 16 to Charleston on the basis of its history, its construction, and the similarity of its carving to that found on bedsteads in the area. Based on the research of Southern scholars, Charleston piecrust tables closely follow English preferences, their distinctive characteristics being an elongated urn carved with acanthus-leaf decoration and surmounted by a tapering shaft, and the flatter arch of the cabriole legs when compared with Philadelphia and New York examples. The acanthus-leaf carving on the knees terminates in a bellflower near the ankle. This table top tilts on a block rather than a bird cage. The column bears a close resemblance to that of the New York example shown in Figure 11.

Fig. 16. Tilt-top tea table, Charleston, South Carolina, 1765–1775. Mahogany; height 27¾, diameter of top 31½ inches. *Museum of Early Southern Decorative Arts, Winston-Salem, North Carolina.*

---

[1] Quoted in Marshall B. Davidson and the editors of American Heritage, *The American Heritage History of the Writers' America* (New York, 1973), p. 48.

[2] Quoted in Russel Blaine Nye, *The Cultural Life of the New Nation, 1776–1830* (New York, 1960), p. 109.

[3] Henry Watson Kent and Florence N. Levy, *The Hudson-Fulton Celebration: Catalogue of an Exhibition of American Paintings, Furniture, Silver and Other Objects of Art, 1625–1825* (New York, 1909), vol. 2, p. 76.

[4] See Morrison H. Heckscher, *American Furniture in The Metropolitan Museum of Art*, vol. 2, *Late Colonial Period: The Queen Anne and Chippendale Styles* (New York, 1985), pp. 188–189, No. 118.

[5] See Richard H. Randall Jr., *American Furniture in the Museum of Fine Arts Boston* (Boston, 1965), pp. 116–118, No. 83.

[6] Other examples of tea tables from the region are found in Brock Jobe and Myrna Kaye, *New England Furniture: The Colonial Era, Selections from the Society for the Preservation of New England Antiquities* (Boston, 1984), pp. 302–304, No. 75, and pp. 304–305, No. 76.

[7] Illustrated in *ibid.*, pp. 286–288, No. 67, and pp. 288–289, No. 68.

[8] For illustrations of the tables see Randall, *American Furniture*, pp. 112, 114, No. 81; Joseph Downs, *American Furniture: Queen Anne and Chippendale Periods in the Henry Francis du Pont Winterthur Museum* (New York, 1952), No. 370; David B. Warren, *Bayou Bend: American Furniture, Paintings and Silver from the Bayou Bend Collection* (Houston, 1975), p. 32, No. 61; Dean A. Fales Jr., *The Furniture of Historic Deerfield* (New York, 1976), p. 150, Fig. 315; and ANTIQUES for April 1957, p. 258, Fig. 17.

[9] *American Furniture*, No. 351.

[10] See, for example, Heckscher, *American Furniture*, vol. 2, pp. 185–186, No. 115; and Warren, *Bayou Bend*, p. 32, No. 60.

[11] Illustrated in Downs, *American Furniture*, No. 373.

[12] See *Master Craftsmen of Newport: The Townsends and Goddards* (Tenafly, New Jersey, 1984), p. xii; see also pp. 222–224, Figs. 5.10, 5.11, 5.12 and Pl. 7.

[13] For examples of these pembroke and card tables, see Oswaldo Rodriguez Roque, *American Furniture at Chipstone* (Madison, Wisconsin, 1984), pp. 294–297, Nos. 137, 138; Jobe and Kaye, *New England Furniture*, pp. 291–294, No. 70; and Downs, *American Furniture*, No. 311.

[14] See Jobe and Kaye, *New England Furniture*, pp. 298–299, No. 73.

[15] A related example, but with a round top, in the Wadsworth Atheneum in Hartford, is illustrated in *The Great River: Art and Society of the Connecticut Valley, 1635–1820*, ed. Gerald W. R. Ward and William N. Hosley Jr. (Hartford, 1985), pp. 233–234, No. 115.

[16] Illustrated in Heckscher, *American Furniture*, vol. 2, pp. 198–200, No. 128.

[17] See Fales, *Furniture of Historic Deerfield*, pp. 148–149, Nos. 310–314.

[18] Illustrated in Heckscher, *American Furniture*, vol. 2, pp. 186–187, No. 116.

[19] For examples of New York tilt-top tea tables see Helen Comstock, *American Furniture: Seventeenth, Eighteenth, and Nineteenth Century Styles* (New York, 1962), No. 399; and Heckscher, *American Furniture*, vol. 2, pp. 196–198, Nos. 125–127.

[20] Darrel Sewell *et al.*, *Philadelphia: Three Centuries of American Art* (Philadelphia Museum of Art, 1976), pp. 75–76, No. 57; and Downs, *American Furniture*, No. 386.

[21] Illustrated in William Voss Elder III, *Maryland Queen Anne and Chippendale Furniture of the Eighteenth Century* (Baltimore Museum of Art, 1968), p. 42, No. 25.

[22] *Charleston Furniture, 1700–1825* (Charleston, South Carolina, 1955), pp. 48–49, and Figs. 130–135.

[23] Cited in Paul H. Burroughs, *Southern Antiques* (Richmond, 1931), p. 79.

[24] Burton, *Charleston Furniture*, p. 48.

"Scollop'd" or "scollopt" top tea tables, now known as "piecrust" tables, were among Philadelphia's most distinctive and popular Chippendale forms. Charles K. Davis collection.

Pl. I. Roundabout chair, Massachusetts, 1740–1760. Walnut; height 30¾, width 27 inches. The scrolled crest has elongated ogee ends. The two-part arm rail is butted at the center. The seat is a slip seat. **Private collection; photograph by courtesy of Israel Sack, Incorporated.**

Chairs with a low semicircular back and a central back leg were made on the Continent at least as early as the fifteenth century. And chairs with a rounded seat, six or eight legs, and eight turned stretchers were made by the Dutch in the East Indies[1] and exported to England and the Continent in the late seventeenth and early eighteenth centuries. Both may have influenced the design of the chair with a square or serpentine seat; low, semicircular back; and central back and front legs often referred to as a corner, or roundabout, chair.[2] These chairs came into fashion in England and America in the late seventeenth and early eighteenth centuries, and in America, at least, acquired many names in addition to roundabout[3]: corner half-moon chair,[4] corner elbow chair,[5] smoking chair,[6] barber's chair,[7] writing chair, desk chair, and combinations of these terms. These various names and the position of a person seated in such a chair support the theory that they were primarily, if not solely, designed for use by men.[8] Certainly only men are shown in them in seventeenth- and eighteenth-century paintings (see Pl. II).

American roundabout chairs

BY HAROLD SACK AND DEANNE LEVISON

Roundabout chairs are listed in many American inventories, but in far smaller quantities than side chairs, and they were more expensive than side or armchairs, especially when they had such embellishments as a serpentine seat front. In 1786 Benjamin Lehman of Philadelphia listed the cost of a mahogany "Corner Chair plain feet and ban^{r}" as £2 10*s.*, with an additional charge of 12*s.* for a serpentine seat front,[9]

Pl. II. Portrait of George Wyllis (1710–1796) attributed to Joseph Steward (1753–1822), 1785–1795. Oil on canvas, 79¾ by 59¾ inches. **Connecticut Historical Society, Hartford, Connecticut.**

Pl. III. Roundabout chair, attributed to the Lathrop-Royce shop, Wallingford, Connecticut, 1745–1760. Maple and ash; height 30½, width 29⅞ inches. The crest has coved ends. The two-part arm rail is butted off-center at the back. The flat arms have scrolled handholds. The splats are tenoned directly into the seat rail, and a flat, molded shoe fits around each of them. The slip seat has notched corners. The side and rear legs have unusual pad feet. The shape of the splats and the distinctive profile of the arm supports, which are pinned to the arm rails from the outside, are features found on other chairs from this part of Connecticut. **Collection of Eric Noah; photograph by Richard Goodbody.**

HAROLD SACK is the president of Israel Sack, Incorporated. DEANNE LEVISON is a consultant to Israel Sack, Incorporated.

Fig. 1. Roundabout chair, New England, 1720–1730. Maple, height 30½ inches. The low crest has notched ends. The two-part arm rail is lapped at the center of the back. The flat arms have scrolled handholds. **Whereabouts unknown; Sack photograph.**

then known as a commode front.

Since roundabout chairs were easy to move, they are recorded in the back bedchamber,[10] the front chamber,[11] front parlor,[12] dining room,[13] sitting room,[14] and kitchen.[15] At the desk the roundabout chair has the advantage of a central front leg, which allows one to move one's feet back unhindered. In eighteenth-century France the *fauteuil de cabinet* offered another solution to this problem. The upper part of the round-backed chair, including the seat, swiveled so that one could straddle a single front leg when desired.

Many roundabout chairs were originally designed as commode chairs and were called three corner'd close chairs,[16] closestool chairs,[17] necessary chairs, and corner chairs for close stool,[18] as well as combinations of these terms. Obviously, chairs upholstered over the seat rail in cloth, rush, or splint could not have been used as commode chairs, and although serpentine-front roundabout chairs were used as commode chairs, those with squared seats were probably much more often so used. Deep skirts, at least on the two front sides, hid the chamber pot on some commode chairs, but on many others no effort was made to disguise their function. For privacy, the chair could always be moved into a corner, away from other activities.[19]

The framework to hold a chamber pot, sometimes including a removable cover, was nailed to the inside of the seat rail, below the slip seat. Quite often this framework has been removed and the aprons concealing the pot have been cut away. When this has occurred, nail holes can usually be found inside the seat rail, and saw marks are evident along the bottom of the seat rail. Sometimes bracket returns have been added.

Fig. 2. Roundabout chair, Rhode Island, 1730–1740. Maple; height 30½, width 27 inches. The crest has cyma ends. The two-part arm rail is butted off-center at the back. The scrolled handholds on the flat arms are slightly chamfered. The front stretchers are more elaborately turned than the back stretchers. **Private collection; Sack photograph.**

The design of roundabout chairs closely followed that of side and armchairs. Splats are in many cases identical to those of related side chairs, their shape simply compressed to fit the shorter distance between seat and arm rail in the roundabout chair.[20] Although the earliest roundabout chairs were probably commissioned individually, as cabinetmaking developed in the Colonies, they were no doubt sometimes made in conjunction with matching sets of side chairs.[21]

The earliest extant style of the American roundabout chair is shown in Figure 3. (The superstructure may or may not be present.) The back is devoid of either slats or splats. A squarish seat frame[22] is supported by three stiles that are joined to the arm rail by round tenons, and a front leg that ends at the seat frame, to which it is joined by a round tenon, or extends slightly above the seat frame (Fig. 1).

Fig. 3. Roundabout chair, Connecticut, 1730–1800. Maple; height 47¼, width 27 inches. The crest under the superstructure has cyma ends. The two-part arm rail is lapped at the center of the back. The single front stretchers are more elaborately turned than the double back stretchers. The chair descended in the Lord and Burr families of Lyme, Connecticut. **Photograph by courtesy of the Chipstone Foundation, Milwaukee, Wisconsin.**

Crests have cyma, serpentine, or blocked ends. They are glued to the arm rails and then secured by rosehead, square, or T-nails. Occasionally they are fastened by screws, but this generally seems to be a later reinforcement rather than the original fastening. The arm rails are generally flat (sometimes chamfered on both top edges) and terminate in simple, flat, bulbous handholds that turn outward. In a few examples the arm supports extend through the arm rail, with which they are flush. The center rear arm support often pierces the arm rail and fits into the crest, while the splats are usually set into shoes.[23] Horizontal slats, when present, conform to the shape of the arm rail. Seats are covered with woven rush or splint. The turnings on the stiles and front leg are like those on related side chairs. Stretchers may all be decoratively turned, or the rear ones may be more simply turned or left plain. Feet may be a continuation of a plain turned leg, a

Pl. Va. Detail of the chair shown in Pl. V, showing vestiges of the framework for a chamber pot.

Pl. V. Roundabout chair, Philadelphia, 1740–1750. Walnut and yellow pine; height 30½, width 28⅞. The low crest has shallow cyma ends. The crest overlaps and unites the arm rails, which end just beyond the splats. The flat serpentine arms end in downward scrolling handholds with volutes. The seat is a slip seat. A detail appears in Pl. Va. **Metropolitan Museum of Art, Rogers Fund.**

ball, or a block and ball in conjunction with a Spanish foot on the front leg or on all four legs (see Fig. 1).

The early chairs were usually made of hard or soft maple, or occasionally cherry, with ash, white oak, birch, white pine, hard yellow pine, or other secondary woods. They were sometimes colored by washes, paint, or graining, and if the owners could afford them, they were fitted with puffy cushions.[24]

Chairs of the above early style with solid or pierced vase-shaped splats were made throughout the eighteenth century. The example shown in Plate III illustrates the evolution of the form. The flat arm rail and the column-and-block turnings of the side and rear legs and arm supports are holdovers of the earlier style, while the vase-shaped splats, slip seat, cabriole front leg with pad foot, and turned cross (as opposed to box) stretchers are innovations. From the beginning, American craftsmen appear to have realized that canting the splats outward from the seat frame made the chair more comfortable.

As the Queen Anne style developed, the roundabout chair followed side and armchairs, with a few interesting exceptions. The style of the crest varied only slightly throughout the eighteenth century and remained generally rather low. Columnar arm supports are related to the stretchers rather than the stiles of related side and armchairs.

The splats and cabriole legs of the side chair in Figure 4 and the roundabout chair in Plate I are quite similar, but the crest of the latter has been enhanced by scrolling at both ends, created by cutting away the wood from the back. The inside of the seat rail of the chairs in Figure 4 and Plate I conforms to the serpentine outside of the rail—the preference in New England—while in New York, Pennsylvania, and the South, the inside of a serpentine seat rail is usually cut straight. Such practices, the presence or absence of corner blocks, the shape of stretchers, and methods of joinery also relate roundabout chairs to contemporary side

Fig. 4. Side chair, Massachusetts, 1740–1760. Walnut; height 35, width 21½ inches. **Art Institute of Chicago, Chicago, Illinois; Sack photograph.**

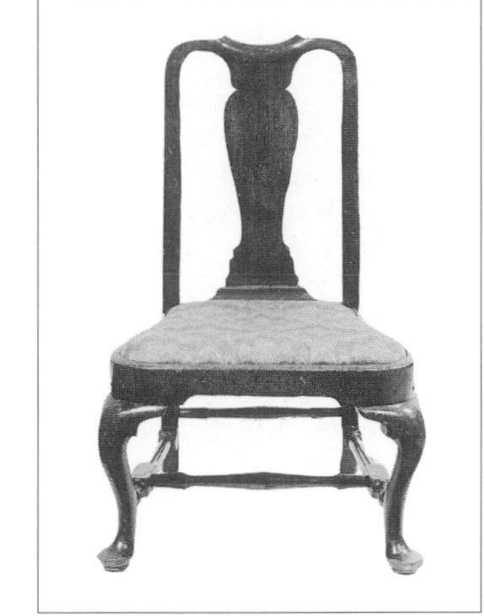

Pl. VI. Roundabout chair, Philadelphia, 1745–1765. Walnut and yellow poplar; height 32⅝, width 27⅝ inches. The low crest has modified stepped ends. The two-part arm rail overlaps at the center of the back. The seat is a slip seat. The chair was designed for a chamber pot. **Henry Francis du Pont Winterthur Museum, Winterthur, Delaware.**

chairs from the same region. On most Philadelphia and some Connecticut roundabout chairs the seat rails are tenoned through the back legs, with the tenon exposed. The cabriole front leg is also tenoned to the seat rail. All joints are secured by two or more pins.

The greatest variation in construction techniques of roundabout chairs is the manner in which the arm rails are connected to each other and to the crest. Most common is a two-piece arm rail meeting at (see Pl. IV) or near the center of the back (see Pl. III) in a simple butted joint. In some cases the central rear arm support merely pierces the arm rail and is glued in place. In others, the arm support continues into the crest. In both cases the joint may or may not be pinned. Sometimes the two pieces of the arm rail are lapped—apparently the preferred joint in the earliest chairs (see Figs. 1, 3). The overlap may be fairly short or as long as six to eight inches. Still other arm supports are joined by a Chinese miter joint, which combines a butted and a lapped joint (Pl. XIII).[25] The butted joint is visible from the front and the lapped joint from the back. Still another joint is exemplified by the Philadelphia chair shown in Plate V.[26] There the arm rails end just after their junction with the splats. The unusually low crest typical of Philadelphia overlaps and completes the arm rail. The serpentine rear arm support is tenoned directly into the crest.

Two other variations on the arm rail have been found in North Carolina and Virginia. A few southern roundabout chairs are known with a one-piece arm rail.[27] A Williamsburg chair of about 1765 attributed to the shop of Peter Scott uses three pieces of wood for the arm rail—two long sections completed at the center by a short section.[28] Such three-part arm rails are found on many English roundabout chairs. A similar three-part arm rail is found on the Rhode Island chair shown in Plate XI.

Some features of roundabout chair design are

common to several regions. For example, the curvilinear arm supports and downward scrolling handholds of Philadelphia roundabout chairs appear in modified form on roundabout chairs attributed to New York.[29] Further, the pronouncedly serpentine seat rails on some Philadelphia examples (see Pl. V) are also found on certain Rhode Island chairs of correspondingly fine quality (see Pl. XI). However, the construction of the seat rail of the Philadelphia chair appears to have no counterpart in Rhode Island. The seat rail of the Philadelphia chair is composed of several pieces, with the two-piece bottom section meeting in a lapped joint above the knee of the front leg. The upper section retains the slip seat. This construction method is also found on many Philadelphia side and armchairs. Also like related Philadelphia side and armchairs, the serpentine-front seat frame of the chair in Plate V is cut square inside.

The Philadelphia chair in Plate VI is typical of roundabout chairs specifically designed as commode chairs. The deep seat frame and aprons conceal the chamber pot. On this chair the aprons end short of bracket returns on the legs. On other examples, particularly from New York, the aprons fill the space between the legs, and the bracket returns are superimposed on the aprons.[30]

The fine quality of some Massachusetts square-seat roundabout chairs is evident in Plate VII, where Chippendale and Queen Anne elements coexist. The relatively high crest rests on finely modeled arm rails that are chamfered on both edges and notched just behind the handholds. The raised pads on the rear and side legs are found on other Massachusetts chairs, and the pierced splats and shaped apron of the seat rail add lightness. This was probably a writing or desk chair; there is no indication it ever served as a commode chair.

The roundabout chair with a superstructure, what John Gloag called a "shaving chair,"[31] is found far more often in England than in America, where it is a relative rarity. These chairs required great skill on the part of the maker, since the superstructure had to be contoured to conform to the rest of the chair. The superstructure of the example in Plate VIII is secured to the crest rail with three tenons, one for each stile

Pl. VII. Roundabout chair, Massachusetts, 1760-1770. Mahogany, height 30¼ width 28½ inches. The crest has cyma ends. The two-part arm rail is butted at the center of the back. The flat chamfered arms are notched behind the scrolled handholds. The seat is a slip seat. The chair descended in the Broughton family of Salem, Massachusetts. Private collection; photograph by John Tsantes.

Pl. VIII. Roundabout chair, Rhode Island or New York City, 1760-1790. Mahogany, maple, and pine; height 44, width 30 inches. The crest below the superstructure has elongated cyma ends. The two-part arm rail is butted at the center. The flat arms have scrolled handholds. The splat in the superstructure is not canted. The seat is a slip seat. **Museum of Art, Rhode Island School of Design; bequest of Charles L. Pendleton. Photography by Cathy Carver.**

Pl. IX. Roundabout chair made by John Gibbs, Newport, Rhode Island, 1742–1750. Branded "GIBBS" on the top of the front leg (see Pl. IXa). Mahogany; height 32, width 27 inches. The crest has cyma ends. The two-part arm rail is butted at the center of the back. The flat arms have scrolled handholds. The seat is a slip seat. **Private collection; Sack photograph.**

Pl. IXa. Detail of the chair in Pl. IX.

and a wider one for the splat, which is wider than those below but does not cant as they do. The addition of a superstructure on this chair results in a bold and dynamic statement that typifies the work of Newport's superb craftsmen.

The chair in Plate IX retains the solid splat of the Queen Anne period but introduces the claw-and-ball foot associated with the Chippendale period. This combination of the old and the new is reversed on the chairs in Plates VII and VIII. The chair in Plate IX is one of the rare roundabout chairs marked by the maker—in this case John Gibbs of Newport.[32]

The chair in Plate X exhibits the rare, if not unique, provision for a candleholder,[33] indicating that it was almost certainly a writing or desk chair.

Roundabout chairs of the kind shown in Figure 6 were made in New York in the latter half of the eighteenth century. Examples exist with both solid and pierced splats and with either flat scrolled handholds or downward scrolling handholds. The quadrant-shaped front seat rail balances the semicircular arm rail and lends itself to the use of three rather than one or four cabriole legs. The depth of the seat rail allows space for a chamber-pot frame, although the pot might still be visible when in place. Most extant chairs of this configuration, including this one, show signs of having been used as commode chairs.

The stylistically more elaborate chairs shown in Plates XI and XII have serpentine seats and four cabriole legs ending in claw-and-ball feet. The finely modeled chair in Plate XI demonstrates the height

Pl. X. Roundabout chair, Massachusetts, 1760–1780. Mahogany; height 31¼, width 31 inches. The crest has cyma ends. The two-part arm rail is butted at the center of the back. The spooned and chamfered arms have scrolled handholds. The arm supports are fluted. The knee of the cabriole front leg is carved with acanthus. The seat is a slip seat. A detail appears in Pl. Xa. **Collection of Mr. and Mrs. Lawrence Fleischman; Sack photograph.**

Pl. Xa. Detail of the chair shown in Pl. X.

of Rhode Island craftsmanship in a Chippendale roundabout chair, just as the chair in Plate V is the Philadelphia equivalent for the Queen Anne style. The Rhode Island chair has two exceedingly rare features: chamfered serpentine arms with dished elbows and interlaced splats that are vertically serpentine (see Fig. 5).[34] The deeply cut serpentine seat frame, cut square on the inside, is blocked at its junction with the side legs, and the cabriole legs have been so shaped that the sap wood of the dense mahogany accentuates the broad, rounded knees.

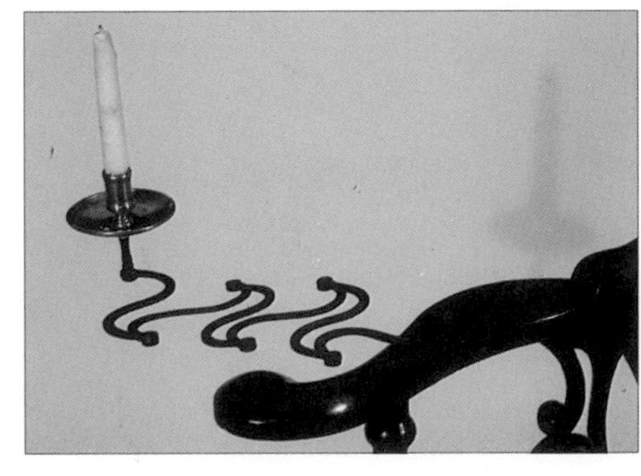

Although carved crests are quite often found on English roundabout chairs, there are perhaps only two American chairs with this characteristic—the one from New York shown in Plate XII and a Massachusetts example.[35] Also quite English is the high block at the base of the arm supports of the New York chair. It has a two-part seat rail joined directly above the shell carving of the central leg. There is no evidence that this chair ever had a frame for a chamber pot.

In the South, Gerrard Hopkins (1742–1800) of Baltimore advertised "Chamber or Corner Chairs" in 1767,[36] but none by him are known today. Many roundabout chairs were made in Virginia and North Carolina, both sophisticated ones with carved cabriole legs and interlaced splats,[37] and simpler ones like the example from Virginia shown in Plate XIII. Rectangular box or cross

Fig. 5. Detail of the chair shown in Pl. XI showing one of the vertically serpentine splats.

stretchers also appear on Pennsylvania and, less commonly, New England roundabout chairs. The inward scrolling handholds, although somewhat unusual, are found on other southern roundabout chairs. Also unusual are the dovetailed inserts in the seat rail covering the bottom of the splats where they are tenoned into the seat rail. The low crest, similar to those on Philadelphia and occasionally on Connecticut roundabout chairs, occurs in the South with various terminations. Southern roundabout chairs with pierced splats reflect the influence of England and the northern American colonies. Certain Williamsburg roundabout chairs made in the shop of Peter Scott have unusual arches cut into the underside of the arm rails on either side of the central back arm support, and a front cabriole leg which extends above the deep seat rail—a feature reminiscent of some New York examples.[38]

The popularity of roundabout chairs diminished markedly at the end of the eighteenth century so that examples in the Federal style are practically nonexistent.[39]

For their help with this article we would like to thank Luke Beckerdite, Michael Brown, Brock Jobe, Gregory Landry, Thomas Michie, James Parker, Bradford Rauschenberg, Susan Swan, and Robert Trent.

1 See John Gloag, *The English Man's Chair* (London, 1964), p. 95; Wang Shixiang, *Classic Chinese Furniture—Ming and Early Qing Dynasties* (San Francisco, California, 1985), p. 97, No. 53; and Luke Vincent Lockwood, *Colonial Furniture in America* (3rd ed., New York, 1926), vol. 2, p. 70.

2 R. W. Symonds, "Walnut and Mahogany Chairs of the Eighteenth Century in the Collection of Mr. Frederick Pike," *Apollo,* August 1939, pp. 48, 49.

3 Brock Jobe and Myrna Kaye, *New England Furniture: The Colonial Era* (Boston, 1984), pp. 360–361, No. 100.

4 William MacPherson Hornor Jr., *Blue Book, Philadelphia Furniture* (Philadelphia, 1935), p. 200.

5 *Ibid.*

6 The Governor's Palace inventory of the personal estate of His Excellency Lord Botetourt (Botetourt manuscripts, Virginia State Library, Richmond).

7 Edgar G. Miller Jr., *American Antique Furniture* (Baltimore, 1937), p. 254.

8 Jobe and Kaye, *New England Furniture,* pp. 360–361, No. 100.

9 Hornor, *Blue Book,* p. 200. See also Martin Eli Weil, "A Cabinetmaker's Price Book," *American Furniture and Its Makers: Winterthur Portfolio 13* (Chicago and London, 1979), p. 183.

10 Hornor, *Blue Book,* p. 200.

11 Dean A. Fales Jr., *The Furniture of Historic Deerfield* (New York, 1976), p. 38.

12 Governor's Palace inventory.

13 *Ibid.*

14 Elisabeth Donaghy Garrett, *At Home: The American Family, 1750–1870* (New York, 1990), p. 136.

15 Fales, *Furniture of Historic Deerfield,* p. 38.

16 Hornor, *Blue Book,* p. 200.

17 "John Parsons...makes all sorts of cabinet work, sitting and easy chairs, closestool chairs, and all other kinds of household furniture..." (*New-York Mercury,* April 22, 1754, quoted in *The Arts and Crafts in New York, 1726–1776,* comp. Rita Susswein Gottesman [New York, 1938], pp. 115–116).

18 Weil, "Cabinetmaker's Price Book," p. 183.

19 Garrett, *At Home,* p. 136.

20 While early roundabout chairs had only stiles, there are no known comparable side or armchairs, all of which have either slats or splats.

21 Herbert Cescinsky, *English Furniture of the Eighteenth Century* (London, n.d.), vol. 2, p. 183; and Jobe and Kaye, *New England Furniture,* p. 360, No. 100.

22 Sometimes the seat frame is shorter from front to back than from side to side (see Patricia E. Kane, *Three Hundred Years of American Seating Furniture* [Boston, 1976], p. 98, No. 80).

23 However, on chairs upholstered over the seat rail, the splats are set into

Pl. XI. One of a pair of roundabout chairs, Rhode Island, 1760–1780. Mahogany and maple; height 31½, width 28¾ inches. The other chair is in the Rhode Island Historical Society in Providence. Both originally belonged to John Brown (1736–1803) of Providence. The crest has cyma ends. The arm rail consists of three pieces, butted and pinned. The serpentine arms are chamfered on both upper and lower edges. They have rare dished elbows and scrolled handholds. The seat is a slip seat. A detail is shown in Fig. 5. **Collection of Peter Eliot; Goodbody photograph.**

Pl. XII. Roundabout chair, New York, 1760–1780. Mahogany and ash; height 31½, width 30½ inches. The scrolled, leaf-carved crest has cyma ends. The two-part arm rail is lapped and pinned at the center of the back. The flat arms have scrolled handholds. The front leg is carved with a shell and pendant. The seat is a slip seat. **Museum of Fine Arts, Houston, Houston, Texas, Bayou Bend Collection, gift of Ima Hogg.**

Pl. XIII. Roundabout chair, Virginia, 1765–1775. Walnut and yellow pine; height 33¼, width 28¾ inches. The crest has short cyma ends. The two-part arm rail is joined with a Chinese miter at the center of the back: butted in front, overlapped at the back. The flat arms with inward scrolling handholds are slightly chamfered. The seat is a slip seat. **Museum of Early Southern Decorative Arts, Winston-Salem, North Carolina, gift of Lucy M. L. Morgan.**

Fig. 6. Roundabout chair, New York, 1760–1790. Mahogany and white cedar; height 31⅝, width 29 inches. The crest with cyma ends overlaps and unites the two arm rails on both sides. The serpentine arms have downward scrolling handholds. The seat is a slip seat. The framework for a chamber pot survives. **Metropolitan Museum of Art, bequest of Cecile L. Mayer, subject to a life estate; photograph by Richard Cheek.**

the seat rail and the shoe, cut out to accommodate them, is affixed after the upholstery has been tacked down.

24 Benno M. Forman, *American Seating Furniture, 1630–1730* (New York and London, 1988), p. 82; and Jobe and Kaye, *New England Furniture*, p. 362, n. 2.

25 See Kane, *Three Hundred Years of American Seating Furniture*, p. 81, No. 60. For the term *Chinese miter* I am indebted to Luke Beckerdite, curator of the Chipstone Foundation, Milwaukee, Wisconsin.

26 Few such chairs exist. For examples, see Morrison H. Heckscher, *American Furniture in The Metropolitan Museum of Art, II, Late Colonial Period: The Queen Anne and Chippendale Styles* (New York, 1985), pp. 87–89, No. 43.

27 Wallace B. Gusler, *Furniture of Williamsburg and Eastern Virginia, 1710–1790* (Richmond, Virginia, 1979), p. 38.

28 *Ibid.*, p. 37.

29 See Joseph Downs, *American Furniture: Queen Anne and Chippendale Periods* (New York, 1952), No. 69.

30 *Ibid.*, No. 62.

31 *English Man's Chair*, p. 94.

32 See Ralph E. Carpenter Jr., *The Arts and Crafts of Newport Rhode Island, 1640–1820* (Newport, Rhode Island, 1954), p. 25; and Ethel Hall Bjerkoe, *The Cabinetmakers of America* (Garden City, New York, 1957), p. 101.

33 When the chair was found the candleholder was missing. However, the hole in the arm and the scrapes across the arm clearly indicate that one had been present originally.

34 Two additional, although rare, features that seem to be exclusive to Rhode Island roundabout chairs are seats upholstered over the seat rail and square legs with stop fluting.

35 In the Henry Francis du Pont Winterthur Museum, Winterthur, Delaware. It is illustrated in ANTIQUES for December 1970, p. 901, Fig. 2.

36 "Gerrard Hopkins, son of Samuel, Cabinet and Chair-maker from Philadelphia at the sign of the Tea Table and chair in Gay Street Baltimore Town Makes and sells...the newest Fashions in Mahogany, Walnut, Cherry-tree and Maple, viz:...Chairs of various sorts such as easy, arm Parlour, Chamber or Corner Chairs, Settees,...N.B. Any of the above Articles to be done with or without carved work" (cited in Marion Day Iverson, *The American Chair, 1630–1890* [New York, 1957], p. 103).

37 Gusler, *Furniture of Williamsburg*, pp. 37–38, Nos. 28, 29.

38 *Ibid.*, p. 38, No. 29.

39 Miller, *American Antique Furniture*, p. 251, n. 4.

Queen Anne and Chippendale armchairs in America

BY HAROLD SACK AND DEANNE LEVISON

The derivation of the term "chairman—occupier of the chair of authority" according to the dictionary—obviously came from the practice of offering a chair to the person chosen to preside over a meeting or to a guest as "the seat of honor." Such chairs were often referred to as "great chairs" and were usually made with arms.[1] The definitions of "armed" or "arming" have been used to describe the function of armchairs. This connotation reinforces the idea that rather than merely being made for the purpose of resting one's arms, these chairs were conceived to be the seat of one "armed" with some form of higher consideration than others present.[2]

The scarcity of wood-backed Queen Anne and Chippendale armchairs in America raises diverse questions. Were some made specifically for use in public facilities outside private houses, such as masters' chairs in fraternal lodges and windsor armchairs in some statehouses?[3] At home, were armchairs made simply to augment other seating forms in parlors, with perhaps some of them intermittently being used in dining rooms as well?[4] Were they primarily made in conjunction with side chairs to form

HAROLD SACK is the president of Israel Sack, Incorporated.
DEANNE LEVISON is associated with Israel Sack, Incorporated.

Pl. I. Armchair Philadelphia, 1740–1760. Walnut and yellow pine; height 41, width of seat 23 1/4, depth 21 1/4 inches. Metropolitan Museum of Art, Rogers Fund.

Pl. Ia. Detail of the armchair shown in Pl. I.

Pl. Ib. Detail of the armchair shown in Pl. I.

Pl. II. Armchair, Philadelphia, 1750–1790. Mahogany; height 44, width of seat 23 3/4, depth 21 1/2 inches. The seat rail is cut out to receive the arm supports. The arm supports terminate in blocks which are serpentine at the back. Another chair of this design is in the Bayou Bend Collection in the Museum of Fine Arts, Houston (illustrated in David B. Warren, **Bayou Bend, American Furniture, Paintings and Silver from the Bayou Bend Collection** *[Museum of Fine Arts, Houston, 1975], p. 27, No. 49).* **Metropolitan Museum, Rogers Fund; photograph by Richard Cheek.**

dining sets? When did two armchairs and four or more side chairs come to be considered a set?

Extant inventories suggest that in the early eighteenth century smaller dining rooms had no more than two armchairs, if any. Later, as dining rooms increased in size, so did the number of dining chairs, although no doubt this was almost entirely due to the addition of side chairs rather than chairs with arms.[5]

Since cabinetmakers' price lists[6] indicate that armchairs were considerably more expensive than side chairs, it is reasonable to assume that cost was a factor in the rarity of the form. Although it has been suggested that in the eighteenth century arms were often added to side chairs for an additional fee,[7] it is interesting to note than in most cases the seats of extant armchairs are usually two or more inches wider than those of matching side chairs. Finally, the very complexity of design and construction exposes the arms and arm supports to breakage, so that many armchairs, once damaged, have presumably been discarded over the years.

Just as the style and design of crest rails, splats, and legs in many cases reflect regional variations, so too do the style, design, and manner of attachment of arms and arm supports.[8]

Philadelphia

More Queen Anne and Chippendale arm-and-side chairs of Philadelphia origin have survived than from any other American cabinetmaking center. Moreover, the proportion of armchairs to side chairs is notably greater than elsewhere, which perhaps accounts for the wider variation in the design of arms, arm supports, and handholds in Philadelphia than other centers. In the Queen Anne period, arms are serpentine in shape and are gracefully sculptured on the top and on the bottom. This contouring, particularly on the bottom of the arm, results in an angled end where the arm connects to the back stile (see Pls. I, II). On chairs with little or no contouring underneath the arms, the inside edge of the arm is nearly vertical at its junction with the back stile. This anticipates the Chippendale style, where in most cases the inside edge of the arm and the inside edge of the stile create a flush vertical plane where they join (see Pls. IV, V). The top of the arms was probably sculptured for the comfort of the elbows. Where the contouring is extreme, the arm appears to rise toward the back along the outer edge. On the more developed chairs, this outer edge is also scribed or beaded.

In most cases the arms are notched at the back to wrap around the outside of the stile, and are held in place by screws which enter from the back with the countersunk screw holes subsequently plugged (see Pls. I, II, IV, V). On some chairs the stiles are also notched to receive the arms (see Pl. V). In a few cases, the arms are tenoned to the stile, and even less frequently they are joined by through tenons (see Pl. III).

In both the Queen Anne and Chippendale periods arms terminate in handholds that may be plain and scrolled downward (see Pl. I, Fig. 2) or may be carved in knuckles or volutes of varying degrees (see Pls. II, V). A distinctive feature of Philadelphia armchairs is the sculpturing of the underside of the arms to form an unbroken flowing line with the arm supports to which they are mortised and tenoned. This sculpturing adds considerable wood surface and consequent strength to an otherwise weak joint (see Fig. 1).

Most of the arm supports of Philadelphia chairs can be divided into three types found in descending order of frequency: scooped, or cobra-headed (see Pls. I, II, V), vertically serpentine (see Pl. IV, Fig. 2), and hoop-shaped, or Chinese (see Pl. III). The scooped supports are usually rounded at the back but vary in the degree of sculpturing on the front. Some are only slightly delineated and others are skillfully carved to a raised bead along the outer edge. On early Queen Anne chairs the scooped arm supports come to a "V" shape at the bottom that beautifully complements the angled end of the arms

Pl. III. Armchair, Philadelphia, 1745–1760. Walnut; height 42 3/8, width of seat 23 3/4, depth 16 1/2 inches. The arms, bulbous at their junction with the stiles, are tenoned through them. The seat frame is unusually shallow and the blocks that terminate the arm supports are correspondingly small. **Henry Francis du Pont Winterthur Museum, Winterthur, Delaware**

Pl. IV. Armchair, Philadelphia, 1760–1770. Mahogany; height 39 3/4, width of seat 25 1/4, depth 19 3/4 inches. The leaf carving on the inside of the arm supports at their junction with the arms is a rarity. The arm supports terminate in blocks which are rounded on the edges and chamfered at the bottom. The chair, with a provenance from the Penn family, is from the same set as that illustrated as Pl. 260 in William Macpherson Hornor Jr., **Blue Book Philadelphia Furniture** *(Philadelphia, 1935; reprinted Washington D.C., 1977).* **Private collection; photograph by courtesy of Israel Sack, Incorporated.**

at their junction with the stiles. All scooped arm supports end in a shaped block which is generally secured to the seat rail by two or more screws, driven from the outside or the inside. The countersunk holes made by those entering from the outside are then plugged. The blocks are usually rabbeted to overlap the seat rail, which, in turn, has been cut away to receive them. The overlap allows the seat frame to act as a base for the arm support. The blocks can be bulbous, angled, or cut in a serpentine shape along the back side and chamfered or rounded along the bottom edge.[9]

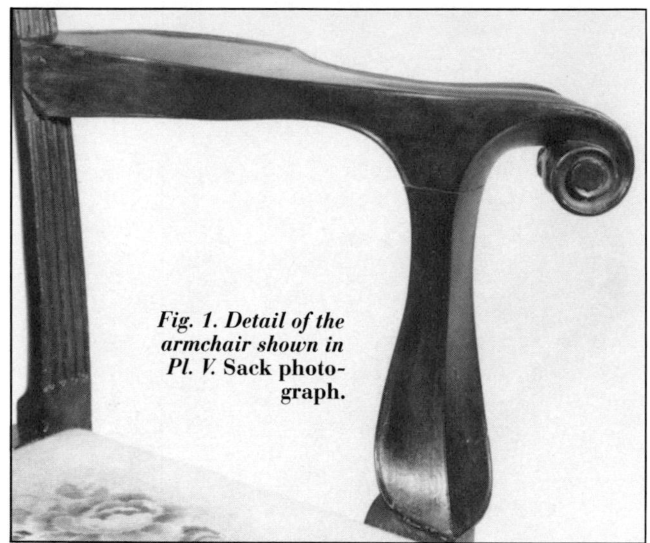

Fig. 1. Detail of the armchair shown in Pl. V. **Sack photograph.**

Pl. V. Armchair, Philadelphia, 1760–1770. Mahogany; height 39 1/2, width of seat 23 3/4, depth 16 1/2 inches. The fluting on the stiles is interrupted at the junction of the arms. The chair descended in the Leedom-Sharp family of Germantown. **Private collection; Sack photograph.**

Vertically serpentine arm supports are found almost exclusively on chairs of the Chippendale period. These supports merely increase in width and thickness as they join the seat frame, to which they are secured with screws driven either from the inside or the outside (see Pl. IV, Fig. 2).[10]

Hooped arm supports are found on both Queen Anne and Chippendale chairs, although they appear less frequently in America than in England. They are quite vulnerable to breakage since the hoop must serve as a handhold, therefore placing the greatest stress on the weakest point, where only a small mortise-and-tenon joint can unite the arm and the support (see Pl. III).

In considering the various styles of Philadelphia armchairs it is obvious that the city's craftsmen produced exciting, vibrant, and skillfully executed examples of the form. The gracefulness and fluidity of the chairs in profile, the integration of the curves of the arms and armrests, and the strength and harmony of the chairs seen from the rear attest to the developed eye of the makers and their patrons.

Maryland

Maryland chairs reflect Philadelphia influence in the design of the backs and legs as well as the arms and arm supports. Although modified hoop shapes are found, the arms are usually serpentine and terminate in scrolled or scrolled and knuckled handholds. The arms are attached to the back stiles and to the arm supports in the same manner as their Philadelphia counterparts. However, rather than scooped, many Maryland arm supports are molded or molded with carved beads. Others are sweeping C-scrolls with bulbous ends which project forward, and still others are vertically serpentine with flattened, rounded blocks. The chair shown in Figure 3 displays the added variation of arm supports which flare outward rather than inward at the bottom. This type of support terminates in a sculptured, rather triangular block with the point at the bottom. The blocks are cut out to fit over the upper half of the molded seat rails, which have been cut away to receive them. On some chairs, such as the one illustrated here, the top edge of the molding forms a graceful fillet behind the block.

New York City

The stylistic variations in surviving New York City armchairs are few compared to Philadelphia. All known examples with cabriole legs have claw-and-ball feet, and all in the Chippendale style have ornamentally carved crest rails. Other English characteristics such as blocked rear feet and handholds carved in the shape of eagles, are much in evidence on New York armchairs.[11] The arms lack the depth of contouring found on Philadelphia chairs, and the inside edge, often rounded in profile, joins the stile closer to its center than to its inside edge. On the chair shown in Plate VI the handholds scroll horizontally rather than vertically and are carved with eagle heads. The arms are cut out so as to wrap

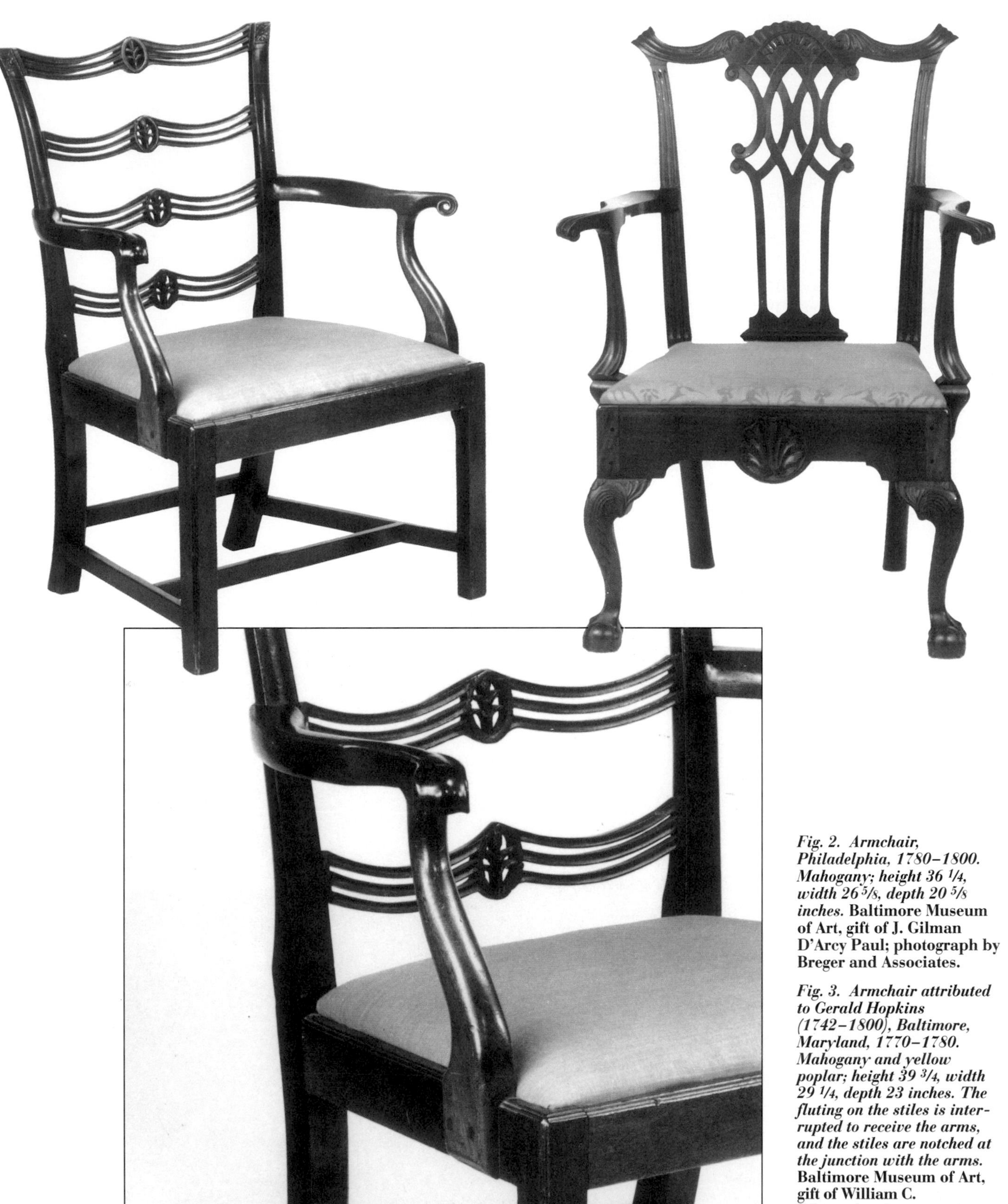

Fig. 2. Armchair, Philadelphia, 1780–1800. Mahogany; height 36 1/4, width 26 5/8, depth 20 5/8 inches. **Baltimore Museum of Art, gift of J. Gilman D'Arcy Paul; photograph by Breger and Associates.**

Fig. 3. Armchair attributed to Gerald Hopkins (1742–1800), Baltimore, Maryland, 1770–1780. Mahogany and yellow poplar; height 39 3/4, width 29 1/4, depth 23 inches. The fluting on the stiles is interrupted to receive the arms, and the stiles are notched at the junction with the arms. **Baltimore Museum of Art, gift of William C. Whittredge; Breger and Associates photograph.**

around the back stiles and are screwed on from the back. The stiles are slightly cut away to receive the arms. There is little contouring on the underside of the arms at their junction with the arm supports so that they meet more or less at right angles in a mortise-and-tenon joint. The arm supports are shaped into simple curves projecting forward at the bottom and are softly rounded along both the front and back edges. They end in blocks which are squared or rounded, and at times also chamfered. On slip-seated chairs the blocks are cut away and lap over the seat rail.[12] On chairs upholstered over the seat rails the rails are often notched to receive the blocks, which are screwed to them (see Pl. VI). Like New York side chairs, the armchairs exhibit the somewhat broad and heavy stance of their Dutch and English prototypes. In profile the backs lack the serpentine shaping of Philadelphia chairs, and the

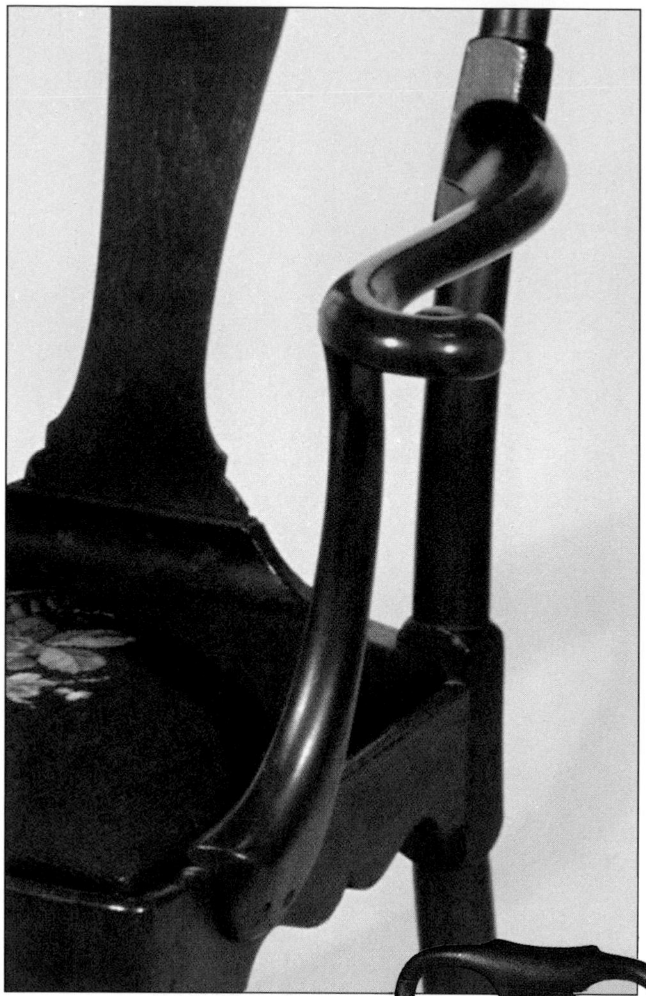

Pl. VI. Armchair, New York City, 1770–1790. Mahogany, oak, ash, and sweet gum; height 39 1/2, width of seat 25 3/8, depth 23 1/2 inches. The arms are rounded at their junction with the stiles. The thick side rails are hollowed on the inside to accommodate the two screws securing each arm support. The chair is part of a set which descended in the Verplanck family. **Metropolitan Museum, bequest of Barbara Bradley Manice; Cheek photograph.**

Pl. VII. Armchair, Rhode Island, 1730–1750. Walnut; height 42 1/2, width of seat 23 1/2, depth 19 1/2 inches. The arm supports are screwed to the rails from outside. This is one of fewer than half a dozen Rhode Island Queen Anne armchairs known. **Private collection; Sack photograph.**

arms appear flatter, resulting in a certain rigidity and absence of movement.

New England

The relatively large number of surviving New England side chairs in the Queen Anne and Chippendale styles makes the paucity of armchairs more astonishing. Surely this cannot be attributed solely to the added cost of this form since elaborate and expensive case furniture was made for many Massachusetts and Rhode Island patrons. Rather, the infrequency of armchairs suggests, but by no means verifies, the theory that the fashion for unupholstered armchairs was not as prevalent in New England as in Philadelphia or New York.

Queen Anne chairs with a crest rail forming twin peaks, a solid splat, a balloon or straight seat, and cabriole legs with pad feet are found in Rhode Island, Connecticut, and Massachusetts (see Pl. IX). Although distinct variations do exist, positive attribution to one colony or another is in some cases difficult. The arms are generally horizontal with the handholds flaring outward. Sometimes the arms are screwed to the stiles, and sometimes they are fastened by mortise-and-tenon joints. The blocks of the arm supports often overlap the top of the seat rails, and where the seat rails are cut away at the bottom in a shallow arch, the back of the block extends below the rail.

Rhode Island

There are probably fewer than a dozen extant Rhode Island armchairs of the Queen Anne and Chippendale periods combined. A rare Queen Anne example (Pl. VII) with rounded stiles exhibits the Chinese influence via England in the sinuous, serpentine back, the blocked plinth at the junction of the arm and the stile, and the beautifully scrolled arms. The arms themselves are cut out to wrap around the side of the blocked section of the back stiles. This blocked section adds strength but is seldom seen on American chairs. The underside of the outward flaring arms is only slightly rounded, forming a flattened junction with the arm supports. The arms terminate in horizontally scrolled handholds. The gently curved arm supports, rounded in profile, broaden and are contoured at the seat rail, which they overlap. The supports are screwed to the rail from the outside. One of possibly the only known pair of armchairs of the Townsend-Goddard school in Newport, Rhode Island, is shown in Plate VIII. The crest rails and splats are typical of Newport and include gadrooning related to that on a kneehole

Pl. VIII. Armchair, one of a pair, attributed to John Townsend (1732–1809), Newport, Rhode Island, 1760–1780. Mahogany; height 38 3/4, width of seat 23 1/4 inches. **Private collection; Sack photograph.**

Pl. IX. Armchair, New England, 1740–1760. Walnut; height 40 1/4, width of seat 23, depth 16 1/4 inches. The arms are slightly notched to fit around the flattened stiles. The block that terminates the arm supports extends below the seat rail at the back, where the rail is cut into an arch. **Sack photograph.**

Fig. 4. Armchair attributed to Eliphalet Chapin (1741–1807), East Windsor, Connecticut, 1772–1774. Cherry; height 39, width of seat 23 inches. The chair was part of the wedding furniture of Anna Barnard, who was married in 1772 and died two years later. **Private collection; Sack photograph .**

Pl. X. Armchair, one of a pair, Massachusetts, 1760–1780. Mahogany. **Private collection; Sack photograph.**

desk signed by and attributed to Daniel Goddard (1697–1764).[13] Like the Queen Anne chair in Plate VII the arms wrap around and are screwed into the back stiles, and the countersunk holes are plugged. The inner side of the slightly serpentine arms is molded, and the handholds flare gently outward before scrolling down in carved volutes. The arm supports are similar in design to those on the chair in Plate VII. They rake decidedly forward at the bottom and are joined to the top of the stop-fluted front legs by pinned mortise-and-tenon joints. This design mirrors that found on marlborough chairs with upholstered backs. Although raked arm supports are found on most Rhode Island chairs, there are one or two examples of molded serpentine supports joined directly to the front of the arm with the molding continuing across the junction.[14]

Connecticut

The armchair in Figure 4 is attributed to Eliphalet Chapin of East Windsor, Connecticut. The side of the molded, serpentine arms wraps around the outside of the stile to which the arm is screwed, with countersunk holes plugged. The contouring of the top and bottom of the arms, the downward sweeping knuckled handholds, and the shaping of the arm as it connects to the arm support reflect Chapin's Philadelphia training. One pronounced deviation is the placement of the blocked serpentine arm supports. On almost all American armchairs, including all other Connecticut examples, the blocks are positioned on the seat rails behind the bracket return of the legs. Chapin's arm supports are instead placed very close to the front corner of the seat frame, whether on chairs with slip seats or those upholstered over the rails. Another unusual feature is the use of round rather than rectangular tenons to connect the arms and the arm supports.[15]

Massachusetts

Relatively few Massachusetts Chippendale claw-and-ball foot armchairs survive (see Pl. X). The arms of these chairs seem to emanate primarily from the sides of the molded stiles and are notched only slightly to overlap the front of the stiles. The elbow rests project outward, and the inner edge of the arm forms only a slight curve. The molded handholds are joined directly to the top of the serpentine arm supports. The supports are cut away to overlap the seat rails, and the top of the molded rails has been removed to receive them.

Other Massachusetts armchairs have more exaggerated serpentine arms and handholds which either scroll downward or horizontally. On such chairs simple forward raking arm supports with squared blocks are connected to the arms behind the handholds with mortise-and-tenon joints.[16] Still other, more elaborate Massachusetts armchairs in the English tradition (see Pl. XI) have serpentine arms with molded elbow rests and tightly scrolled handholds with little buttons projecting from either side. The arms rest directly on top of carved, serpentine arm supports, and join the fluted stiles roughly at their center.

Massachusetts ladder-back armchairs differ from their Philadelphia counterparts in the design of both the arms and the arm supports. The bowed or slightly serpentine arms connect directly to the molded arm supports and the molding is continued to incorporate the junction (Pl. XII). The arm supports are either notched to fit over the seat rails (Pl. XII) or they slip into dovetailed grooves cut into the rails. The arms are sometimes screwed on from the back of the stile (Pl. XII) and sometimes attached by dovetails cut into the stiles.

Portsmouth, New Hampshire

Until recently, chairs with double-scrolled arm supports like the one shown in Figure 5 were ascribed to Newburyport, Massachusetts. Now chairs with such supports, either with wooden backs or upholstered backs, are believed to have been made in Portsmouth, New Hampshire. The molded serpentine arms are rounded across the top as they enter the front of the stiles. In most cases they are not cut away to wrap around the stiles. The handholds, which extend beyond the arm supports, curve outward and have simple bulbous terminations. The blocks of the arm supports are screwed to the seat rail from the outside. Other less sophisticated chairs from this region have curved arms flattened above and below, of which the handholds are merely wider extensions of the arms rounded off across the front.

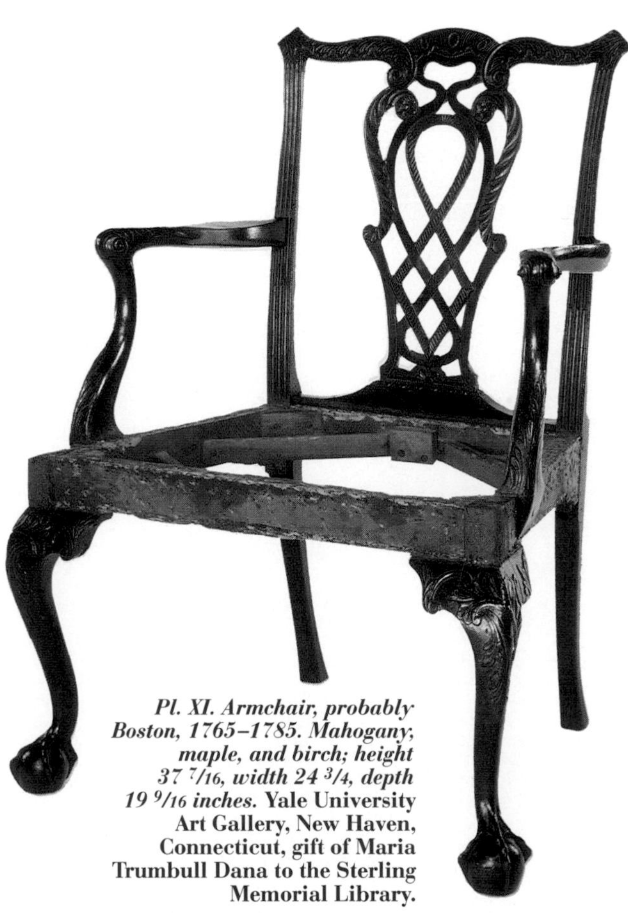

Pl. XI. Armchair, probably Boston, 1765–1785. Mahogany, maple, and birch; height 37 7/16, width 24 3/4, depth 19 9/16 inches. **Yale University Art Gallery, New Haven, Connecticut, gift of Maria Trumbull Dana to the Sterling Memorial Library.**

The arm supports of these chairs end in blocks without scrolled ornament.[17] Many Portsmouth armchairs are upholstered over the seat frame.

The South

In the South, tea tables and dressing tables in a relatively pure Queen Anne style can be found from Virginia to South Carolina. Armchairs by and large reflect English Chippendale design. Arms and arm supports vary both in shape and in method of attachment to the stiles and seat rails. The chair shown in Plate XIII is one of several of the same type attributed to the North Carolina coastal town of Edenton.[18] The serpentine arms, flattened on top from the elbow rests to the handholds, are carved in shallow relief with geometric panels and floral handholds. The arms are tenoned into and pinned through the stiles. The block of the serpentine arm supports extends only halfway down the seat rail. The supports are rabbeted to fit over the molding of the seat rail, and are held in place by hand-wrought finishing nails driven from inside the seat frame. On a group of chairs attributed to the shop of Peter Scott (1694–1775) in Williamsburg, Virginia,[19] the arms are connected to the stiles by dovetail joints visible from the back of the stile, and by screws. Stylistically, these chairs are related to New York Chippendale chairs, particularly in the curve of the arm supports and the carved handholds.

Other armchairs from Virginia south through Charleston, South Carolina, have arms which are conventionally attached by screws from the back of the stile and arm support blocks which extend to the bottom of the seat rails.[20]

Pl. XIII. Armchair, North Carolina, possibly Edenton, 1745–1765. Mahogany, beech, and cypress; height 39 1/4, width of seat 24 inches. **Museum of Early Southern Decorative Arts, Winston-Salem, North Carolina.**

Pl. XII. Armchair, Massachusetts, 1780–1790. Mahogany; height 37 1/2, width of seat 23, depth 19 7/16 inches. **Sack photograph.**

---

1 Peter Thornton, *Authentic Decor, The Domestic Interior 1620–1920* (New York, 1984), p. 25.

2 Joan Gloag, *A Short Dictionary of Furniture* (London, 1969), p. 18.

3 Lemuel Adams (w. 1792–1800) billed for "20 Mahogany Armed chairs" in 1819 for the new statehouse in Hartford, Connecticut.

4 It is known, for example, that chamber-pot chairs were found in both bedrooms and dining rooms.

5 A notice by William Rush in the *Pennsylvania Packet* for December 22, 1778, states, "Was left in the house of the subscriber...six mahogany chairs, hair bottoms; eighteen walnut leather bottom chairs; one arm chair with blue damask bottom, and two rush-bottom ones" (quoted in *The Arts and Crafts in Philadelphia, Maryland, and South Carolina, 1721–1785*. Alfred Coxe Prime [Topsfield, Massachusetts, 1929], p. 191). Listed in the inventory of Mary Bull of Charleston, South Carolina, dated January 20, 1770, are "55 Mahogany chairs, 2 easy chairs, 2 arm chairs, 8 walnut chairs" (quoted in E. Milby Burton, *Charleston Furniture, 1700–1825* [Charleston, 1955], p. 12).

Fig. 5. Armchair, Portsmouth New Hampshire, 1760–1790. Mahogany, maple, and white pine: height 38 7/16, width 26 7/8, depth 20 3/8 inches. The arms are tenoned into the stiles and the arm supports are tenoned into the arms. The tenons are not pinned. **Photograph by David Bohl. Courtesy of SPNEA, Boston.**

6 See, for example, the price list of Benjamin Lehman (b. 1760) of Philadelphia for "Chairs With Crooked Legs" of January 1786, cited in William Macpherson Horner Jr., *Blue Book Philadelphia Furniture* (Philadelphia, 1935; reprinted, Washington, D.C., 1977), p. 210.

7 *Ibid.*, pp. 215–216.

8 Here the term "arm support" is used for the eighteenth-century term "stump" to describe the element connecting the seat rail to the arm. Similarly, the term "handhold" is used for the period grip or pummel. We wish to thank Robert F. Trent, the curator of the furniture at the Henry Francis du Pont Winterthur Museum in Winterthur, Delaware, for advising us on this nomenclature.

9 Because Philadelphia balloon-seat chairs are constructed with a deep inner frame, the blocks are by necessity screwed in from the outside.

10 On chairs upholstered over the seat rails the rails are cut out in varying degrees to receive the blocks at the end of the arm supports.

11 Eagle-head handholds have been found on some Massachusetts chairs. See *American Antiques from the Israel Sack Collection*, vol. 3 (Washington, D.C., 1972), p. 614, No. 1398.

12 A New York armchair with a Van Rensselaer family history appears to have blind dovetails connecting the blocks to the seat rails (see Joseph Downs, *American Furniture, Queen Anne and Chippendale Periods in the Henry Francis du Pont Winterthur Museum* [New York, 1952], Pl. 52).

13 Illustrated in ANTIQUES for May 1984, p. 1103, Pl. II.

14 See Christopher F. Monkhouse and Thomas S. Michie, *American Furniture in Pendleton House* (Providence, Rhode Island, 1986), p. 174, Fig. 116.

15 See ANTIQUES for May 1986, p. 1092.

16 See Downs, *American Furniture*, Pl. 56; and David B. Warren, *Bayou Bend, American Furniture, Paintings and Silver from the Bayou Bend Collection* (Museum of Fine Arts, Houston, Texas, 1975), Fig. 83.

17 Illustrated in ANTIQUES for May 1978, p. 1103, Fig. 6.

18 See John Bivins Jr., *Furniture of Coastal North Carolina 1700–1820* (Winston-Salem, North Carolina, 1988), pp. 156–160.

19 See Wallace B. Gusler, *Furniture of Williamsburg and Eastern Virginia 1710–1790* (Richmond; Virginia, 1979), p. 28.

20 See Bivins, *Furniture of Coastal North Carolina*, Pls. 7.19, 7.19a, and 7.59; and Gusler, *Furniture of Williamsburg*, Pls. 60, 61, 101.

The Richard Edwards Pier Table

P6266: Chippendale mahogany claw and ball pier table. The creative genius of a master craftsman and carver combined to fashion a supreme achievement of Philadelphia artisanship. The rhythmic composition of the pierced frieze complements the equally rhythmic grace of the leg carving and gadrooned top border. Made by Thomas Tufft for Richard Edwards. Philadelphia 1775.

Ht: 33¼″ Wd: 35 1/16″ Dp: 17 1/8″

This table is a part of a suite of furniture made by Thomas Tufft for Richard Edwards in 1775. Included in this suite is a pedimented high chest of drawers, dressing table and set of chairs.

Illustrated and described in ''Antiques'' Magazine, October 1948 pgs. 246-247.

The following page numbers are a continuation from Volume IX.

Americana — A New Dimension

May 16, 1990

In May 1980, our 34th brochure heralded this past decade and made a prediction about the future for American antiques. It read in part as follows:

"A few fundamental questions must be considered. First, will the academic and investment interest in American antiques continue to advance? Second, where will the market direction come from? In regard to the academic interest, there seems to be little doubt that the stream of publications will increase. The public interest likewise is being widened by the increased number of exhibitions pertaining to Americana. The opening of the newly expanded American Wing at the Metropolitan Museum of Art cannot fail to have a tremendous effect on the study and appreciation of the American artist-craftsmen.

All this expenditure of energy and effort to bring the American story to the world, as well as the nation, cannot fail to kindle and rekindle the developing interest. This must result in new converts, and with the ever diminishing supply coming to market, we have no doubt that the monetary value will be adequately reflected."

As we enter the decade of the 1990's, these predictions have proved to be dramatically prophetic. Interest in Americana has soared to new heights. A number of scholarly books, publications and articles and museum research have added to our knowledge of the achievements of our craftsmen. Several museums, led by the opening of the DeWitt Wallace Gallery at Colonial Williamsburg have expanded or opened new American galleries.

Perhaps the most dramatic development was our purchases of the Nicholas Brown secretary-desk and the Richard Edwards pier table. These sales were recorded world-wide and placed American furniture on a level commensurate with fine arts such as paintings and sculpture. The fact that we are able to present objects that exhibit both authenticity and artistic merit at affordable prices becomes more appealing in the light of an expanding market. The opportunity to build, or add to, a fine collection has never been greater. We believe that we provide unique resources to offer such opportunities as the selections in this brochure clearly demonstrate. Such results are possible because:

1. Our concentration is exclusively on superior quality and we have the expertise that enables us to judge top quality and avoid mistakes.

2. The reacquisition of fine items sold by our firm in the past provides a source of supply uniquely available to us.

3. Our ability to grade an item properly within a broad spectrum in its category assures our clients of fair pricing and guidance to suit individual collecting goals.

4. The good will, contacts, and wide awareness of our aggressive buying habits brings to us a considerable percentage of the choice objects that become available.

5. Finally, our resources and the ability to purchase and own outright adds to our impact in acquiring the choicest objects to appear on the market.

As we enter the 1990's it is rewarding to know that each of our predictions for the past decade has materialized. Unprecedented changes in the world political scene with democracy supplanting restrictive governments result in international focus on American values. Since our Colonial achievements clearly reflect these values, the impetus to collect things uniquely American increases concurrently.

It is gratifying to know that our firm has played, and continues to play, a part in increasing the care and appreciation of the efforts of our early artisans. In the ensuing decade we pledge to them and to you this same dedication.

We are open during regular business hours and welcome your visit at anytime.

Albert M. Sack   Harold Sack   Robert M. Sack

Deanne Levison Associate

The William Trask Chest

P6264: Pilgrim oak chest with hinged lid and one drawer. The front contains three panels of geometric moldings flanked by split spindles. The drawer also flanked by spindles. Triglyphs, bosses and diamonds complete the decorations, all of which are original. Massachusetts, circa 1660-1680.

Ht: 30″ Wd: 47½″ Dp: 21¾″

The chest descended in the family of Capt. William Trask of Salem, Massachusetts who came to this country as early as 1628 and was one of the founders of Salem. It remained in the Trask family until we purchased it.

Vignette of chest in Trask homestead.

Front View Trask Homestead, Boston St., Salem, Mass.

The interior of the Trask Homestead.

P6234: Sheraton mahogany crib with finely turned posts. Mellow brown patina. One side is removable.Massachusetts, circa 1800-1810.

Ht: 37½″ Lg: 44¼″ Wd: 23″

P6182: Assembled pair of birch rush seat corner chairs. The front legs end in platformed wafer pad feet and are flanked by fine ball and ring turned stretchers. The chairs are virtually identical and are undoubtedly from the same shop. Massachusetts, circa 1740-1760.

Ht: 31¼″ Wd: 28½″ Dp: 25″

P5008: Early pine decorated blanket chest with one drawer and lift top. Original engraved tear drop brasses and escutcheons. The decoration of exotic birds, trees and leaves on a red background is typical of a small group attributed to Robert Crosman. Tauton, Massachusetts, circa 1725-1730

Ht: 32¾″ Wd: 38¼″ Dp: 18½″

Ex-collection Mitchel Taradash.
Illustrated in ''American Painted Furniture'' Dean A. Fales, Jr., plate 45.

P6262: Early pine painted and decorated court cupboard. The decoration consists of black and ochre crescents on a salmon-wash background with black balusters and framing members. Original tear drop brasses center rayed decorated panels on the upper section. Hampton, New Hampshire, circa 1730-1740.

Ht: 51 3/4″ Wd: 37 5/8″ Dp: 19 1/4″

Illus. Nutting ''Furniture Treasury'' #471
Illus. Nutting ''Furniture of the Pilgrim Century'' #143
Illus. ''Antiques'' Magazine, April 1930, page 315

P6261: Chippendale maple slant top desk of rare small scale, original brasses and stepped back interior. New England, circa 1760-1780. This desk is not a miniature but rather was probably designed for a child.

Ht: 39½″ Wd: 25½″ Dp: 17½″ Wr. lev.: 27¾″

DETAIL

P6270: William and Mary mahogany tavern table. The table represents a supreme achievement of the turner's art, as well as a rare early use of mahogany. The top is octagonal with a molded edge and the legs are outsplayed in both directions. Fine bronze patina. Massachusetts, circa 1720-1740.

Ht: 26½″ Wd: 32½″ Dp: 21¾″

P6258: Sheraton mahogany upholstered bergere-type chair. Concave back with mahogany bowed crest and frame, bulbous turned arm supports, turned tapered legs and bowed seat frame. One of thirty chairs made by George Bright. Boston, Massachusetts, circa 1797 for the Boston State House.

Ht: 32½″ Wd: 23″

P5516: Queen Anne walnut stool back chair. The upholstered back has a yoke shaped crest, the slip seat frame has a scalloped apron. The bold cabriole legs have pointed knees. Rhode Island or Massachusetts, circa 1740-1760.

Ht: 38¾″

P6243: Queen Anne cherry library or work table. The frame contains one long and one short drawer. The top pivots on wooden pins. The turned tapered legs end in platformed pad feet. Choice amber patina. Pennsylvania, circa 1750-1760. The table exhibits more refinement than the usual rural examples.

Ht: 30″ Wd: 54″ Dp: 34″

P2259: Queen Anne mahogany drop leaf table with squared cabriole legs ending in drake feet. The table has the rare feature of a drawer in each end, both of which retain the original bail brasses. Philadelphia or vicinity, circa 1750-1770.

Ht: 28 3/4″ Lg: 43 3/4″ Wd: 59 5/8″ open; 17 3/4″ closed

P2139: Queen Anne San Domingan mahogany bonnet top highboy. This masterpiece expresses the unique greatness of American Queen Anne design by virtue of its slender stately proportion, its understated elegance, and its superb patina. The depth of the surface tones with its light and dark undertones add to its grandeur. The brasses, one finial and one pendant drop are original. The carved shell drawer and C-scrolled marginal knee carving suggest Newport origin, but Boston origin cannot be discounted. The piece was brought from New York to Nova Scotia by Jacob Miller during the Revolution. Newport or Boston, circa 1740-1750.

Ht: 7′2″ Wd: 39½″ Dp: 22¼″

P6236: Hepplewhite mahogany inlaid card table with bowed front and serpentine sides. The front is centered by an inlaid Grecian urn on a green background framed in a rectangular mitred panel. The line inlaid tapered legs are surmounted by oval floral inlaid paterae. Light mellow brown patina. Attributed to William Lloyd, Springfield, Massachusetts, circa 1780-1800.

Ht: 29½″ Wd: 36″ Dp: 17″

P6248: Mahogany and gilt banjo clock. The original eglomise panels are of exceptional quality and interest. The base panel depicts an allegoric rendering of the New Republic. The waist panel is inscribed "A. Willard, Jr." The dial is inscribed "Warranted for Colonel Isaac G. Reed" and the clock is crested by a finely sculptured carved and gilded eagle. The clock was made by Aaron Willard, Jr. for Colonel Isaac Gardner Reed for his mansion in Waldboro, Maine, circa 1815-1825.

Ht: 35½″ Dp: 10″

P6263: Chippendale walnut claw and ball foot four shell armchair. The serpentine shaped arms with powerfully rolled scrolled knuckle terminals are magnificently modelled. Choice mellow brown patina. Philadelphia, circa 1760-1780.

Ht: 40½″ Wd: 30½″

P6272: Chippendale mahogany claw and ball foot block front slant top desk. The piece epitomizes the bold character fashioned by one of the finest artisans of Boston and Salem. The claw and ball feet are finely sculptured and the block and shell carved interior is of high development. The pine tree brasses and side carrying handles are original. Massachusetts, circa 1760-1780.

Ht: 45″ Wd: 42″ Dp: 21½″ Wr. lev: 32

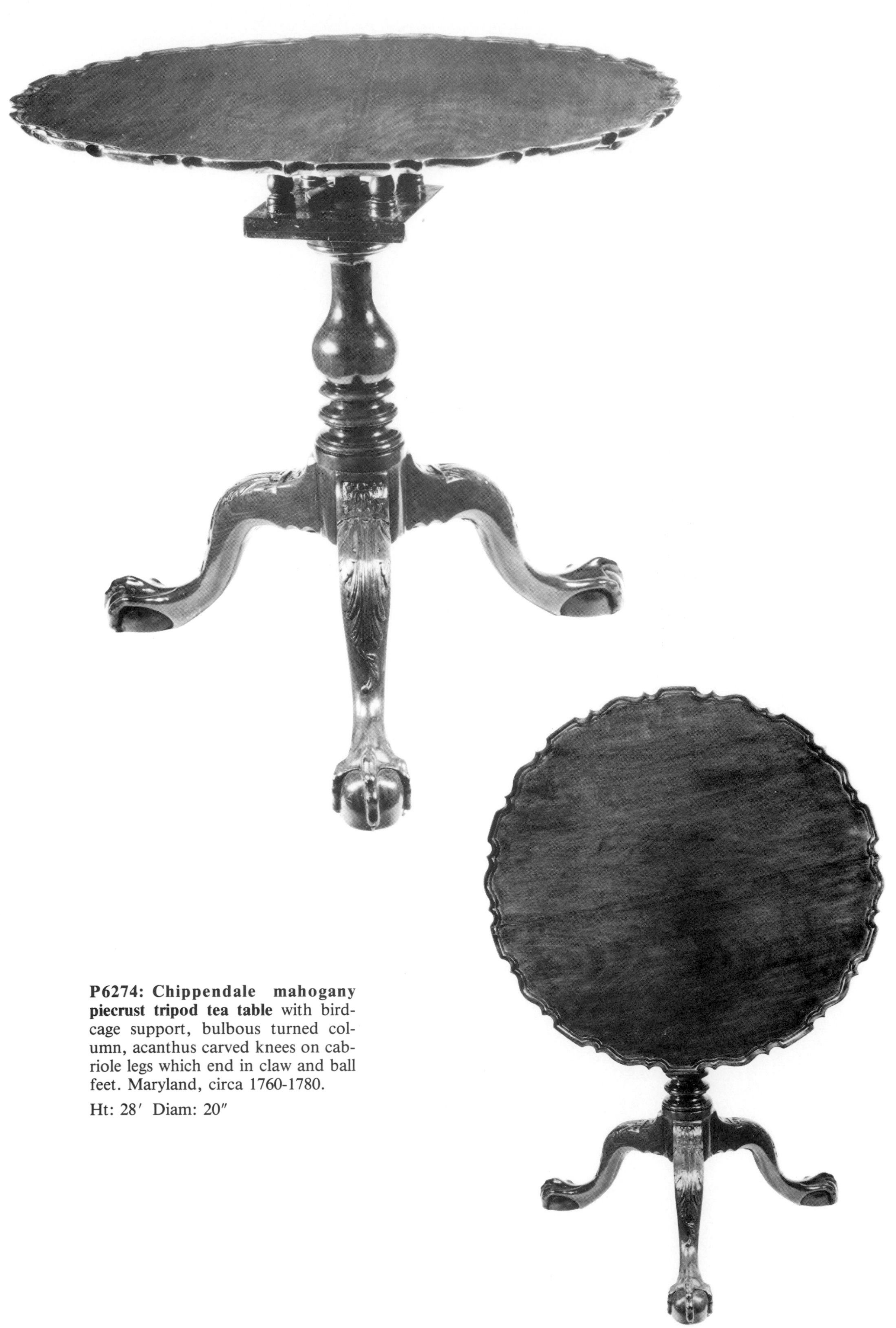

P6274: Chippendale mahogany piecrust tripod tea table with bird-cage support, bulbous turned column, acanthus carved knees on cabriole legs which end in claw and ball feet. Maryland, circa 1760-1780.

Ht: 28′ Diam: 20″

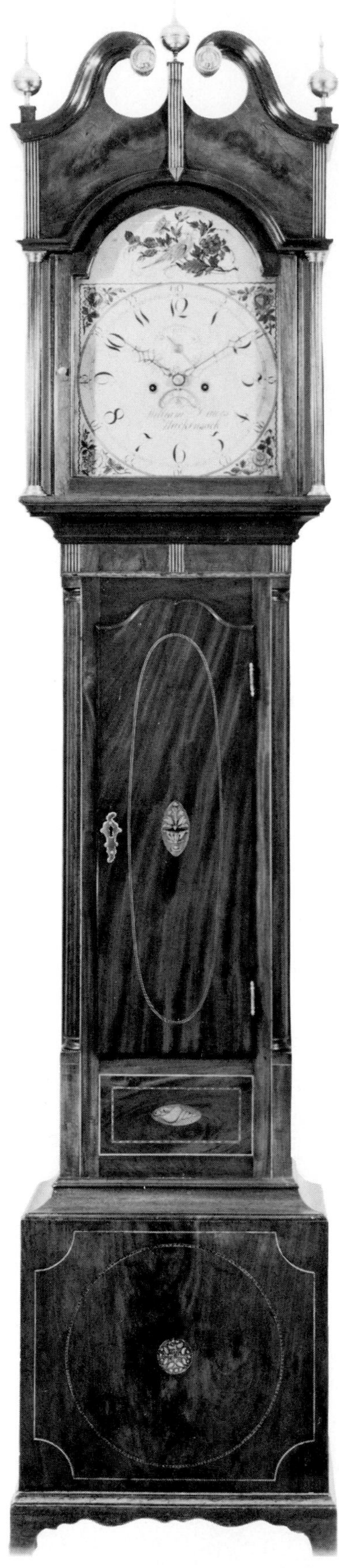

P6227: Oval miniature on porcelain depicting a bust portrait of George Washington. The original brass frame has a molded beaded border surmounted by a ribbon. A brass standard in the back serves as a stand to display in an upright position. Painted by Jean-August Edouard Lienard (1779-1848) and signed J. Lienard. French for the American market, circa 1810.

Ht: 6½″ Wd: 5″

P6273: Hepplewhite mahogany inlaid tall case clock. The case finely inlaid with urn, shell and floral paterae; the enamelled dial inscribed William Dawes, Hackensack (New Jersey), circa 1790-1810.

Ht: 8′ Wd: 19 7/8″ Dp: 10″

P6253: Hepplewhite mahogany mirror of scrolled outline with scrolled ears and double line inlay framing the original glass. The scrollboard is centered by an eagle inlaid patera depicting the Symbol of the New Republic — an eagle with shield and 17 stars. Fine old patina. New York, circa 1810-1815.

Ht: 46″ Wd: 19½″

P6252: Chippendale mahogany claw and ball foot side chair bearing the original label of Benjamin Randolph, at the Sign of the Golden Ball, Chestnut Street, Philadelphia. The splat is of strapwork formation, the crest with molded scroll ears, the knees with shell carving. Mellow brown patina. Made by Benjamin Randolph. Philadelphia, circa 1760-1780.

Very few labelled pieces by Benjamin Randolph are known and thus the chair is an important document. Other labelled chairs of the set are in the family and one is in the Winterthur Museum.

Ht: 38″

P3592: Pair of Queen Anne side chairs. Each chair has a vase shaped and spurred splat, horseshoe slip seat and finely modelled cabriole legs with turned stretchers. Norwich, Connecticut, circa 1740-1760. The chairs are of the same pattern as the Governor Lyman armchair. See "Craftsmen and Artists of Norwich" 1965, page 52.

Ht: 40½″

P6238: Chippendale cherry oxbow bureau with blocked ends and double ogee bracket feet. The dynamic impact of this piece is created by a compact case, bold blocking which continues on the inner brackets of the ogee feet and a bold overhang. The drawers retain the original brasses. Connecticut, circa 1760-1780.

Ht: 30¾″ Wd: 33¾″ Dp: 20¼″

Ex-collection of Charles F. Montgomery

P3334: Queen Anne San Domingan mahogany drop leaf dining table. The table exhibits the expert craftsmanship of the Goddard-Townsend school and has finely modelled platformed pad feet. The dovetailed cross brace and original blocks associate it to the Townsend family of cabinetmakers. Newport, Rhode Island, circa 1740-1770.

Ht: 28″ Lg: 48″ Wd. open: 48″ Wd. closed: 15″

Illustrated in "Master Craftsmen of Newport" by Michael Moses, pg. 46.

P6276: Queen Anne walnut tray top tea table of rare diminutive size. A graceful example in fine state of preservation with fine old patina. Massachusetts, circa 1740-1760.

Ht: 26′ Diam: 25½″ × 17¾″

P6277: Queen Anne walnut side chair. The finely modelled crest rail with its four volutes flanking the shell completes a beautiful curvilinear composition that ranks with the finest expressions of the Philadelphia chairmaker's art. The condition and color of the chair are beyond criticism. Philadelphia, circa 1750-1760.

Ht: 42¼″

Illustrated and described in the ''Girl Scout Loan Exhibition 1929'' catalog #565. On loan at the Metropolitan Museum by Mr. and Mrs. Allen R.A. Bradley 1934 & 1935.

Ex-collection Charles K. Davis

P6213: Hepplewhite mahogany secretary-desk. The top "drawer" is fronted by an oval figured satinwood or birch panel. The front drops on brass quadrants to reveal a writing interior. The glass panels are framed in mullions of geometric formation. Salem, Massachusetts, circa 1790-1810.

Ht: 79½″ Wd: 40″ Dp: 18½″

P6222: Queen Anne maple highboy with fan carved drawer in upper and lower case section. The cyma shaped apron is centered by "salamander" scrolls typical of the Dunlap school. The bottom drawer is actually one deep drawer with a facade simulating two rows of drawers including the fan carved center. New Hampshire, circa 1760-1780.

Ht: 78¼″ Wd: 37¾″ Dp: 19″

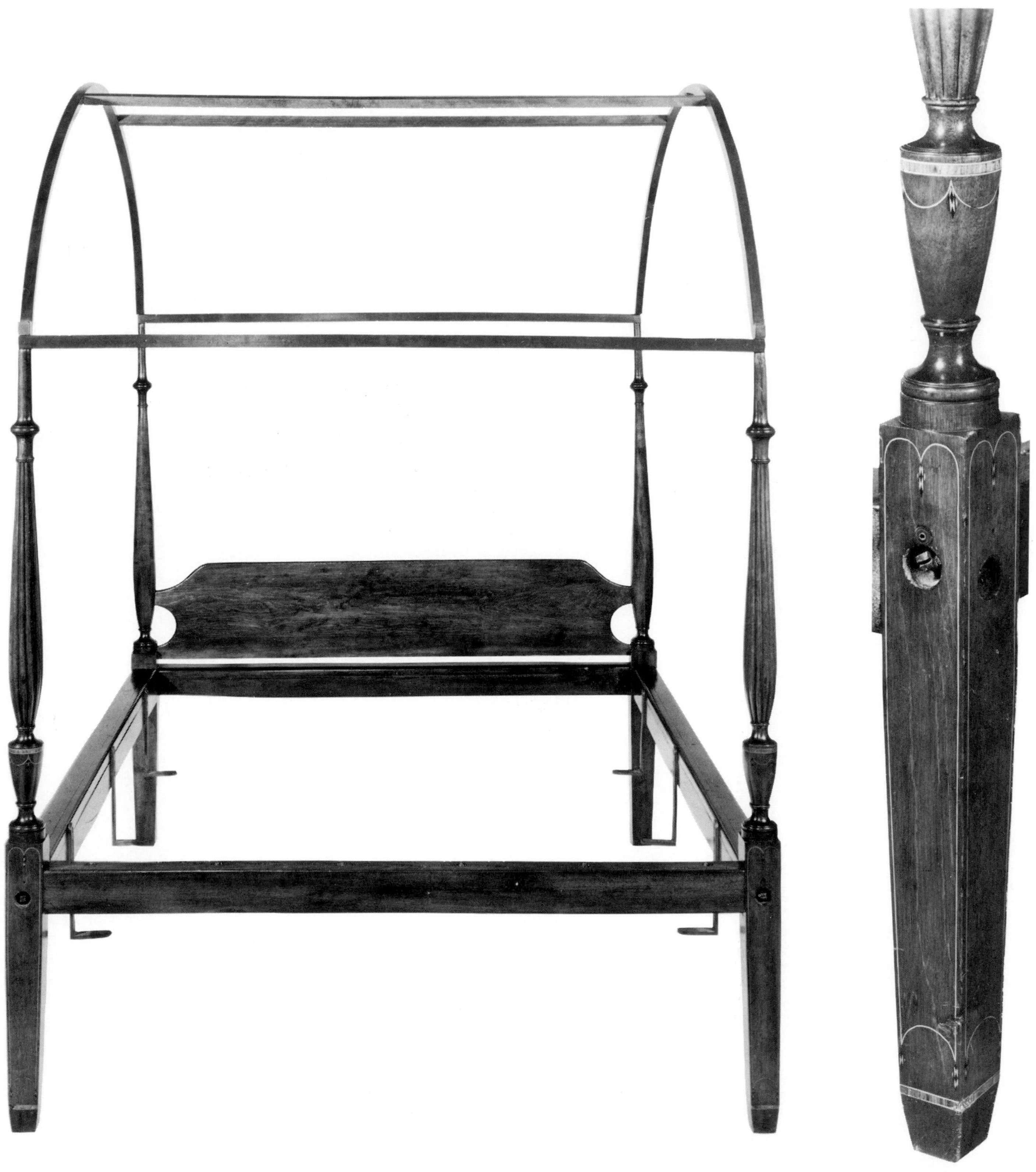

P4599: Hepplewhite mahogany, birch, and cherry four post canopy bed, superbly designed foot posts with finely inlaid urns, the drapery has a diamond checkered motif at each point, that motif repeated on the line inlaid leg and the top and crossbanded cuff, the bulbous reeded posts are tastefully swelled, the bowed tester, rails and shaped headboard are the originals, the footposts are turned in simpler fashion. Beautiful amber patina. The diamond checkered inlay is a favored motif in Portsmouth furniture. Portsmouth, New Hampshire, circa 1780-1800. This bed was sold by Israel Sack in the 1950's and recently reacquired. Israel Sack always considered it the finest Hepplewhite bed he ever owned.

Ht: 6′10″ Lg: 6′4″ Wd: 57″

P6280: Chippendale mahogany tall clock with brass spandrelled moon phase dial inscribed "John Wood, Philadelphia." The case exhibits the combined efforts of a master carver and cabinetmaker from that center. The superb proportions, wood grain and brilliantly carved scrollboard exhibit an excellence rarely achieved in contemporary examples. Made by John Wood, Jr., Philadelphia, circa 1770-1780. Descended in the Haskins family of Philadelphia.

Ht: 8′7″ Wd: 18¾″ Dp: 9″

P6246: Chippendale mahogany claw and ball foot oxbow bureau with blocked ends. The chest exhibits the craftsmanship and proportion of a master craftsman of the Boston or Salem group. Its beauty is enhanced by the exceptional swirled grain that has taken on a golden tone. Massachusetts, circa 1760-1780.

Ht: 32½″ Wd: 36¾″ Dp: 21½″

P6229: Hepplewhite mahogany Martha Washington upholstered armchair or lolling chair. The tapered legs and arm supports are molded, the molding extending on to the serpentine shaped arm. Serpentine crest. Massachusetts, circa 1780-1800.

Ht: 44 3/8″ Wd: 23 1/2″

P6278: Classical gilt convex mirror surmounted by a black sculptured eagle flanked by cornucopia. American or English, circa 1810-1820.

Ht: 40½″ Wd: 28″

P5982: Sheraton mahogany sewing table, octagonal frame with one drawer and a sewing slide, the top with beaded border. The delicate tapered reeded legs with bulbous feet are capped by acanthus carved capitals. Choice bronze patina. Salem, Massachusetts, circa 1800-1810.

Ht: 27¾″ Wd: 20¼″ Dp: 15½″

P6255: Classical birds-eye maple and maple veneer work table with lyre pedestal. The case has two drawers and turret corners, the outsplayed legs with brass casters emanate from a square platform. Beautiful mellow patina. Philadelphia, circa 1810-1815.

Ht: 30″ Wd: 18″ Dp: 13½″

P6250: Hepplewhite mahogany inlaid demiline card table. The plinths are inlaid with paterae depicting the American eagle, symbol of the New Republic. The bellflower inlay of the tapered legs is of rare design but related to a table of Southern origin (''Antiques'' April 1974, page 882). Circa 1800-1810.

Ht: 30″ Wd: 36″ Dp: 18″

P6245: Sheraton mahogany dining table consisting of 2 demilune console ends, each with a drop leaf. The veneered frame with beaded edge border has a carved rosette in the plinth above each leg. The reeded legs have acanthus carved capitals and feet with ring turned collars. The table is attributed to Ephraim Haines, Philadelphia, circa 1800-1810.

Ht: 29″ Lg: 89½″ Wd: 47½″

Ex-collection George Horace Lorimer.
Illustrated Hornor "Blue Book of Philadelphia Furniture" plate 399.

P6259: Pair of Hepplewhite mahogany shield back side chairs. Each splat contains a carved drapery anchored by a carved urn and fleur-de-lis and carved rosettes. Tapered reeded legs with beaded cuffs. New York, circa 1780-1800.

The chairs are apparently from the set of identical design that descended in the family of Sir William Johnson of Schenectady, New York. Those chairs were sold in the Philip Flayderman Sale, 1930, Catalog 446.

Ht: 39″

P5344: Hepplewhite mahogany inlaid corner washstand, outsplayed legs, one drawer. Massachusetts, circa 1790-1810.

Ht: 38¼″ Wd: 22½″ Dp: 16″

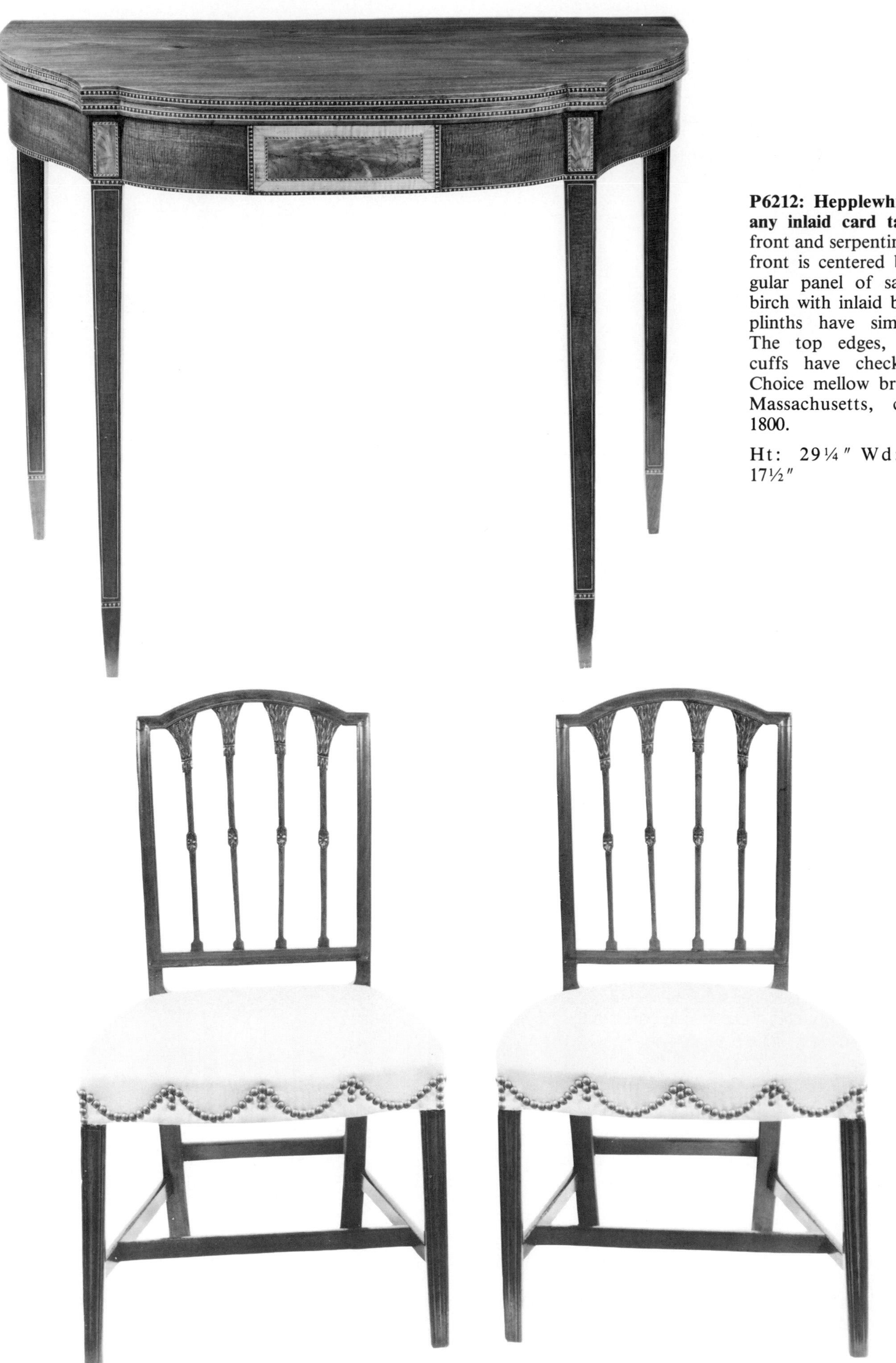

P6212: Hepplewhite mahogany inlaid card table, bowed front and serpentine sides. The front is centered by a rectangular panel of satinwood or birch with inlaid borders. The plinths have similar panels. The top edges, apron and cuffs have checkered inlay. Choice mellow brown patina. Massachusetts, circa 1780-1800.

Ht: 29¼″ Wd: 36″ Dp: 17½″

P6275: Assembled set of 8 Sheraton mahogany side chairs. The design is of typical Salem formation, the slats with carved rosettes and flaring acanthus carved capitals. Salem, Massachusetts circa 1800-1810.

Ht: 36″

P6225: Set of four Chippendale chairs with stop fluted legs consisting of two arm and two side chairs. To our knowledge, this set contains the only pair of Newport Chippendale armchairs known to exist. The gadrooned carving appears on the Toland kneehole desk (Nutting plate 627) and the Daniel Goddard kneehole desk (Moses-Sack "Master Craftsmen of Newport" page 265). The interlaced splats have a loop formation and a floral carved motif centers the crest. The sculptured arms end in scrolled terminals. Fine mellow brown patina. Attributed to John Townsend, Newport, Rhode Island, circa 1760-1770.

Armchairs Ht: 38¾″ Wd: 23½″. Side chairs Ht: 37¾″

Ex-collection King family, Newport, Rhode Island.
Illustrated "Antiques" Magazine December 1947, page 430.

P6241: Hepplewhite mahogany inlaid dressing table. The hinged lid reveals an interior with a framed adjustable bevelled mirror flanked by lidded compartments; arched apron, line inlaid tapered legs. New York, circa 1790-1810.

Ht: 31″ Wd: 36 1/8″ Dp: 20 1/2″

The family history records its descent in the family of Theodore Ely.

P5181: Pair of Hepplewhite mahogany inlaid card tables with rectangular frames and canted corners. Bellflower and pellet inlaid legs. Massachusetts, circa 1780-1800.

Ht: 28½″ Wd: 35¾″ Dp: 17½″

P6230: Rare diminutive Queen Anne walnut tray top tea table with candleslides. The tray top is formed of two crotch grained book matched boards contained within coved moldings connected by ogival retaining moldings. The graceful bandy legs add to its appeal. Connecticut, circa 1740-1750

Ht: 26¾″ Wd: 24¼″ Dp: 18″

Descended in the family of Ebenezer Gay of Suffield, Connecticut. Illustrated in "Antique Furniture in Suffield, CT," by Charles S. Bissell, 1956, plate 15.

P6221: Hepplewhite mahogany inlaid serpentine front sideboard. The beauty and placement of the rich crotch grained veneer, the book, quarter fan and bellflower inlays and the inlaid lily of the valley paterae are all enhanced by a golden patina. The design relates to the masterpieces in the Karolik Collection, Museum of Fine Arts, Boston and the High Museum in Atlanta and epitomizes the heights achieved by New York artisans of this period. Attributed to William Whitehead, New York, circa 1780-1800.

Ht: 42″ Wd: 72″ Dp: 29″

P6239: Hepplewhite mahogany inlaid bowfront cabinet corner washstand. The richly figured crotch grain of the drawers and doors are accentuated by broken-bar inlaid borders, diagonal inlay along the edge of the top and shell paterae on the legs. Choice mellow patina. Massachusetts, circa 1780-1800.

Ht: 37″ Wd: 22″ Dp: 14″

P6242: Sheraton mahogany secretary-desk. The finely veneered door of the upper case hinges down to reveal a compartment of satinwood drawers, pigeonholes and document partitions and to form a writing flap. Slender reeded legs. Made by Duncan Phyfe or a contemporary of equal rank. New York, circa 1800-1815.

Ht: 58¾″ Wd: 33″ Dp: 24″ Wr. Lev: 28″

P4154: Sheraton mahogany inlaid five-legged card table, serpentine front and sides with turret corners. The frame is centered by a veneered crossbanded panel flanked by birds-eye panels repeated on the sides and plinths. The apron and top edge is bordered by lunette inlay. Boston, Massachusetts, circa 1800-1810.

Ht: 30″ Wd: 34″ Dp: 18¼″

This table was in the Robb Collection (Sack Col. V, pg. 1227) and recently re-acquired.

Illustrated "Antiques" Magazine April 1968, pg. 487.

P4021: Chippendale mahogany curly maple slant top desk. The bracket feet and center pendant have spurred fishtail scrolls. The unusual interior is formed of four bands of small drawers in a stepped formation. Original brasses. New Hampshire, circa 1770-1790.

Ht: 41″ Wd: 36″ Dp: 18¾″ Wr. lev: 28¼″

P6268: Rare Sheraton cherry end table. The original gray veined marble top is enclosed in a line inlaid frame with dark and light fan quadrants. The frame, enhanced by birds-eye maple panels and plinths and bordered by lunette inlay, contains one drawer. Reeded legs end in bulbous tapering feet. Boston, Massachusetts, circa 1800-1810.

Ht: 28¾″ Wd: 19¼″ Dp: 17¾″

P6249: Hepplewhite cherry end table. One drawer with original knob flanked by oval paterae. The square top is inlaid with a large oval patera depicting a gypsy moth in green background and has fan inlaid spandrels in the corners. Connecticut, circa 1780-1800. The low height makes this table useful as an occasional table.

Ht: 23¾″ Top: 17″ × 17¾″

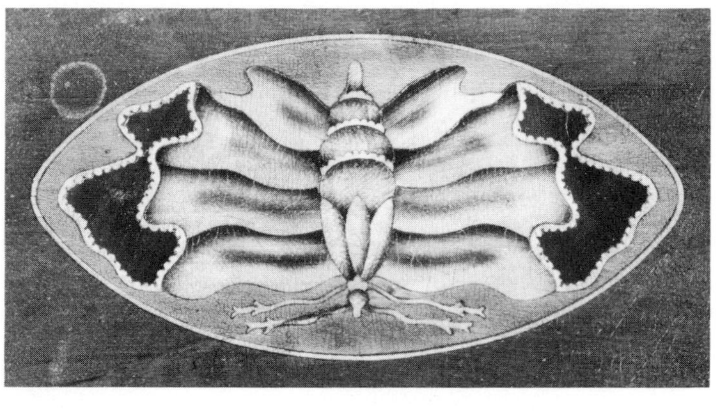

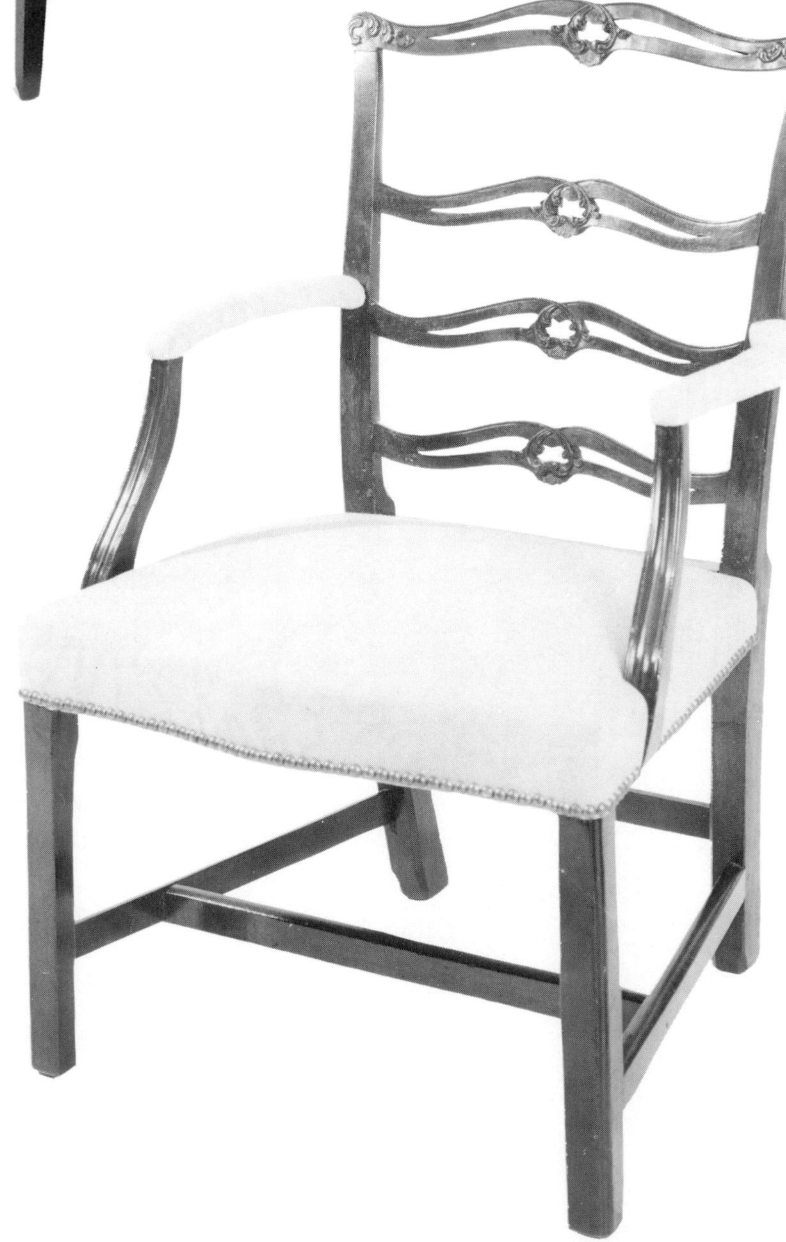

P4944: Chippendale mahogany ladderback armchair. Acanthus carving on the ears of the crest rail is repeated in the center of each of the four pierced slats. The serpentine overupholstered arms are a rare variation. The legs and stretchers are molded. Massachusetts, circa 1780-1790.

Ht: 37½″ Wd: 24″

P-6247: Hepplewhite mahogany inlaid tall clock made by Simon Willard, Roxbury, Massachusetts circa 1793. A family plaque inside the door reads "Given by John Goddard as a wedding present to his son Benjamin Goddard 1793". A complete line of descent accompanies the clock. A companion to this clock, also made by Simon Willard for the Goddard family, is in the Museum of Fine Arts, Boston.

This is one of the finest cases on clocks by Simon Willard. The lunette inlay and the superb fretwork are exceptional.

P6240: Queen Anne curly maple slant top desk. The piece is distinguished by the exuberantly figured striped grain and finely modelled cabriole legs. The drawers of the stepped interior repeat the striped grain of the case. North Shore, Massachusetts, circa 1760-1780. A related desk is in the Edison Institute.

Ht: 43″ Wd: 38″ Dp: 18″ Wr. lev: 32½″

P6210: Hepplewhite mahogany inlaid card table with bowed front and serpentine sides. The front is formed of finely figured crotch grain flanked by curly maple panels within inlaid borders. The tapered legs have delicate bellflower and pellet inlay. Choice mellow brown patina. Massachusetts, circa 1780-1800.

Ht: 29½″ Wd: 39″ Dp: 18¾″

P6195: Hepplewhite mahogany sofa. The crest has a raised panel conforming to the crest panels on Philadelphia Federal side and armchairs. Bulbous reeded arm supports and tapered legs. Philadelphia, circa 1790-1810.

Ht: 34½″ Wd: 73″ Dp: 31″

P6251: Pair of Hepple-white mahogany shield back side chairs. In each chair three vertical slats emanate from an acanthus carved crescent and flare to bowed branches centered by carved tulips in punchwork backgrounds. Tapered legs end in spade feet. The chairs are in superb condition with an original nut brown patina and the original horsehair covering. Salem, Massachusetts, circa 1780-1800.

Ht: 38″

P6257: Hepplewhite cherry inlaid linen press. A beautifully proportioned piece with broken arch top, inlaid rosettes and a central triangular keystone. The diamond and loop inlaid frieze, the line inlaid pilasters and doors and the oval panels at the base add interest to the design. Light amber patina. Southern, circa 1790-1810.

Ht: 96″ Wd: 40″ Dp: 21¼″

P6220: Pair of Classical mahogany card tables, each table consists of a rectangular frame with canted corners. Within the frame are birds-eye maple panels with central chased brass mounts and carved rosettes in the corners. The double reeded columsn have globular sections wtih incised rings, a motif repeated on the leg supports.

Ht: 29¼″ Wd: 35″ Dp: 18″

P-6223: Sheraton mahogany writing table. The frame has one row of three drawers. The top has an adjustable writing tablet behind which is a veneered panel flanked by boxed compartments. New York, circa 1800-1810.

Ht: 37½″ Wd: 39″
Dp: 25½″ Wr. lev: 30¾″

“The Pause That Refreshes”

Quite often political and economic events of cataclysmic proportion deflect a perspective in relation to the arts. History provides some direction for all of us to use as a measuring stick in order to gauge the future. It is well to bear in mind that most of the great creations of the Colonial period were wrought during a time of political and social upheaval. Even the early Colonists who were deprived of the comforts of life took time to embellish, in artistic form, some of their furnishings.

It is foolish to ignore the ripple effect of major events, yet these same events are filled with opportunities for those who have a long-range vision. In our more current history the beginning of the 80's, which began in recession, seemed ominous to those who were paying heed to the epochal occurences around them, both politically and financially. Yet this period marked the beginning of one of the greatest eras of esthetic interest and price increases. So too we feel that the opportunities that present themselves at this point in world events are great for those who are not faint hearted.

It is historically true that during unsettled periods the prices of average pieces, whether referring to real estate or art, are soft due to lack of consumer interest. Yet, the acquisition of objects which approach the status of choice or, in the case of art, masterpiece levels results in greatly enhanced artistic satisfaction as well as financial rewards.

While we do not sell investments per se, our experience has proven that the highest quality objects not only ride out these temporary storms, but seek and attain new levels. One must always go back to the fundamentals inherent in the law of supply and demand. It is obvious that the number of choice pieces of American furniture presenting themselves in the marketplace is diminishing. The old axiom of small supply and large demand is the necessary ingredient for high prices. Demand is based on interest, desire and affordability. As evidenced from the past, we can be assured that the interest and desire of both museums and individuals for objects representative of our American heritage will not diminish. The only missing ingredient is the unknown element of affordability. World financial analysts have predicted an explosion of national and international prosperity in the decade of the 90's. If these predictions materialize, disposable wealth accumulated by interested people will certainly result in a competitive situation for the very best.

Our faith and confidence in the future is based not on predictions, but on factual historic evidence. We will continue to seek out — to acquire and to reacquire — choice examples of American craftsmanship as demonstrated in this brochure.

Albert M. Sack — Harold Sack — Robert M. Sack

Deanne Levison Consultant

P-6096: Queen Anne San Domingan mahogany drop leaf table with round top. The cabriole legs with ridged knees have bulged voluted knee returns and end in crisp wafer pad feet. The apron has a cyma outline. Fine nut brown patina. Massachusetts, circa 1750-1770.

Ht: 27¾″ Top: 42″ × 41¼″

P-6185: Queen Anne maple armchair of transitional form. The finely modelled back and molded serpentine arms indicate the handiwork of an urban chairmaker. The arms are supported by block and bulbous turned legs ending in Spanish feet. Massachusetts, circa 1740-1760.

Ht: 41″ Wd: 23″

P-6298: Chippendale San Domingan mahogany drop leaf table of rare small size, cabriole legs with ridged knees ending in raised ball feet and elongated talons. The table is branded IS indicating its ownership by Israel Sack in the 1920's. Salem, Massachusetts, circa 1750-1780.

Ht: 28″ Top: 36¼″ × 35¾″

P-6111: Queen Anne walnut side chair with overupholstered horseshoe shaped seat. Mellow old patina. Massachusetts, circa 1740-1760.

Ht: 39¾″

P-6292: Rare Chippendale mahogany small scale card table. The case contains one drawer with original brass handles and gadrooned carved apron. The top of fine mottled mahogany has turret and cyma shaped corners. The cabriole legs end in claw and ball feet. New York, circa 1760-1770.

Ht: 28″ Wd: 31″ Dp: 13½″

P-6293: Chippendale mahogany slant top desk, the fret carved interior relates to examples by Thomas Affleck and Philadelphia contemporary artisans, fine golden patina. Philadelphia, circa 1760-1780.

Ht: 43″ Wd: 40″ Dp: 21 1/2″ Wr. lev: 30 1/2″

P-6297: Chippendale mahogany side chair with hairy paw and ball feet. The knees have asymmetrical leaf carving. The interlaced vase shaped splat of tassel, diamond and strapwork design, as well as the asymmetrical knee carving are features typical of Boston design. The four taloned hairy paw feet appear on a labelled Benjamin Frothingham desk (''Furniture of Historic Deerfield'' Dean A. Fales, Jr., page 230) and suggest an attribution to that maker, Charlestown, Massachusetts, circa 1760-1780.

A chair of this design and probably of this set is in the Henry F. DuPont Winterthur Museum (Downs, plate 151).

Ht: 36 3/4″

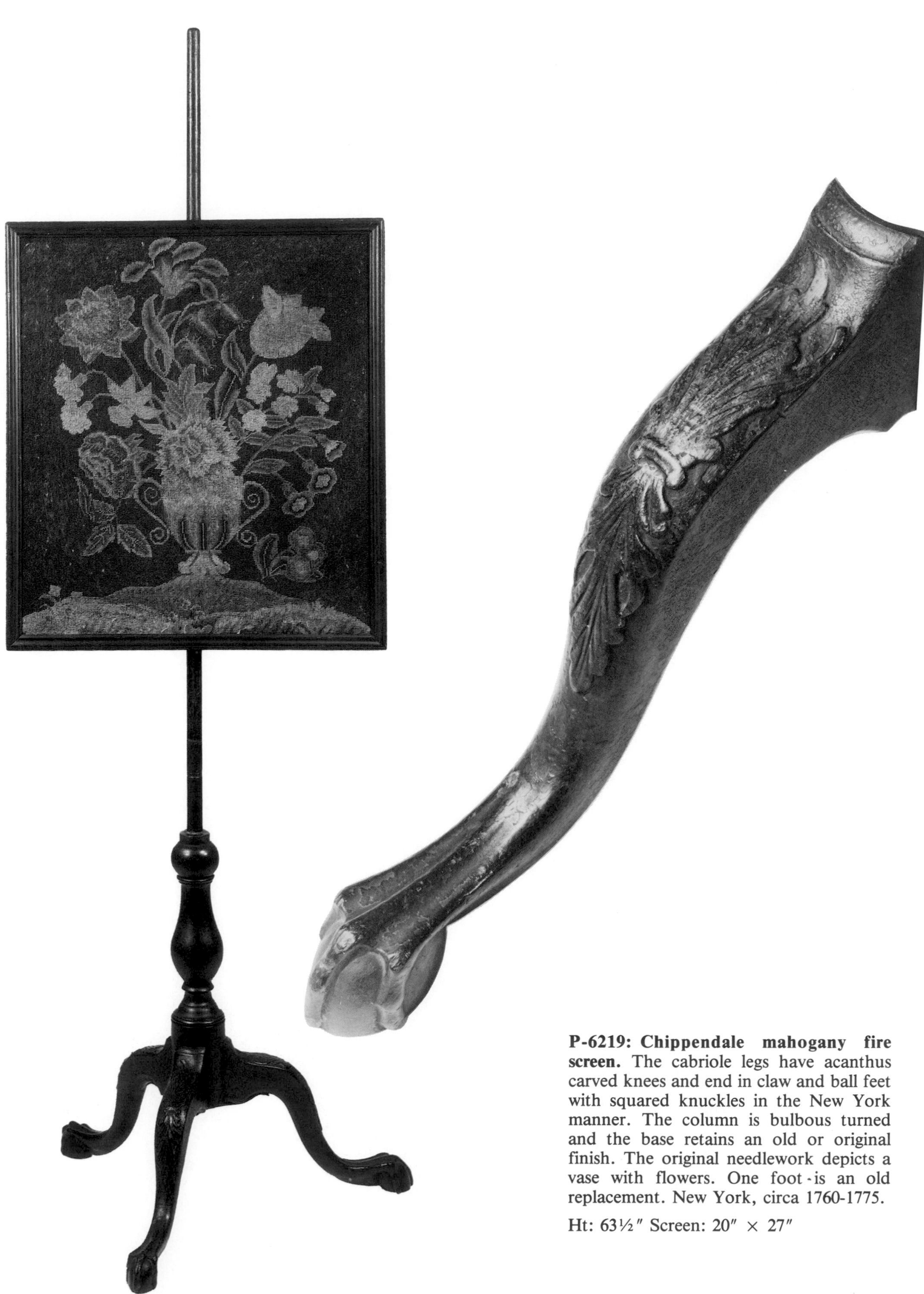

P-6219: Chippendale mahogany fire screen. The cabriole legs have acanthus carved knees and end in claw and ball feet with squared knuckles in the New York manner. The column is bulbous turned and the base retains an old or original finish. The original needlework depicts a vase with flowers. One foot-is an old replacement. New York, circa 1760-1775.

Ht: 63½″ Screen: 20″ × 27″

P-6287: Chippendale mahogany candlestand with oval tilt top, urn column, cabriole legs ending in ridged platformed feet. Choice bronze patina. Salem, Massachusetts, circa 1760-1780. One of the finest quality stands of this form. Descended in the Munro family of Lexington, Massachusetts.

Ht: 27¾" Top: 20½" × 14 7/8"

P-6007: Hepplewhite mahogany secretary. The cornice with raised center plinth and end plinths, all with brass finials. The two glazed doors of the upper section enclose pigeonholes for letters and three shallow horizontal drawers. The lower case, with slanted fold-out writing surface, is comprised of four graduated drawers of matched grained mahogany veneer with cross-banded and cock-beaded edges. The shaped apron joins outsplayed French feet. Massachusetts, circa 1790-1800.

Ht: 82 1/2" Wd: 40" Dp: 19 3/4"

P-6289: Chippendale mahogany mirror with scrolled chest and base and voluted ears. The scrollboard centers a pierced and gilded shell. American or English, circa 1760-1780.

Ht: 32″ Wd: 14″

P-6205: Chippendale mahogany side chair. The crest rail has a floral carved center and is supported by a strapwork splat with voluted terminals. The form in this development is more often seen with cabriole legs. Massachusetts, circa 1760-1780.

Ht: 38″

P-6128: Chippendale mirror with gilded phoenix in the pediment cut-out. The vibrancy of the scrolled pediment is repeated on the lower section and a gilded inner mirror border accentuates the molded frame. Of richly grained walnut veneer. American or English, circa 1760-1780.

Ht: 36″ Wd: 16″

P-6290: Chippendale mahogany Martha Washington or lolling chair with serpentine crest, nicely scooped arm rests, molded arm supports and square legs. Massachusetts, circa 1770-1780.

Ht: 45 3/4″ Wd: 27 1/4″ Dp: 20″

P-6058: Queen Anne maple bonnet top highboy with fan carved drawer in upper and lower case sections. The lower case has a rare fan carved motif centering the apron. Few maple examples exhibit the fine proportions and craftsmanship this highboy displays. North Shore, Massachusetts or Coastal New Hampshire, circa 1750-1770.

Ht: 7′3″ Wd: 37¼″ Dp: 20½″

P-6294: Chippendale mahogany bombe front kneehole desk. The top drawer is fitted with compartments. The recessed cupboard is fronted by a panelled door with a mitered serpentine frame reflecting the shape of the bottom edge of the shallow drawer above. The strong ogee bracket feet, the rich mottled grain of the mahogany and a beautiful golden patina enhance this rare form. Massachusetts, circa 1760-1780.

Ht: 31″ Wd: 33 1/2″ Dp: 23 1/4″

P-6301: Queen Anne walnut lowboy, concave blocked scooped center drawer. Massachusetts, circa 1740-1760. This piece is in the finest state of preservation, retaining the original finish, bat wing brasses and pendant drops.

Ht: 30½″ Wd: 35¼″ Dp: 20¼″

P-6291: Sheraton mahogany side chair. The back is of delicate design with drapery and rosette central splat supporting an undulating molded crest rail. The reeded legs end in spade feet. New York, circa 1800-1810. Ex-collection Harry Weeks, Framingham, Massachusetts. Illustrated Nutting "Furniture Treasury" Vol. II, plate 2389. A chair of this design, and probably of this set, is in the Mabel Brady Garvan Collection, Yale. Illustrated in "300 Years of American Seating Furniture"; Patricia E. Kane, plate 148.

Ht: 36 1/2″

P-6102: Queen Anne walnut wing chair, finely shaped back with peaked serpentine crest, boldly curved cabriole legs with ridged knees ending in platformed pad feet, chamfered maple rear legs, original light brown patina. Massachusetts, circa 1750-1770.

This chair was illustrated in the frame showing the original linen undercover in American Antiques from Israel Sack Collection Volume IX, page 2479.

Ht: 46″ Wd: 34 1/2″ Dp: 20 1/4″

Designed by Benjamin Latrobe

P-6311: Pair of Greek Revival painted and decorated side chairs. Entablature crests crown the central caned section of the back. The seat, also caned, is held within an apron carved to simulate fringe along the lower edge and the outsplayed saber legs reflect the Grecian klismos form. Elaborately and skillfully painted in red, black and ochre and gilded with designs of rosettes, anthemia and winged animals exemplifying the highest fashion of the day. In the finest state of preservation. Designed by Benjamin Latrobe. Made by Thomas Wetherill. Philadelphia, circa 1800-1810.

Ht: 34 1/2″

Chairs of this design are illustrated in the following publications:

''Classical America 1815-1845; The Newark Museum'' Cover of book and No. 28.

''American Painted Furniture 1660-1880'' Dean A. Fales, Jr., page 149.

Matched Pair of Godda

P-5894: Ex-collection Mitchel Taradash
Illustrated "American Antiques from Israel Sack Collection" Vol. VIII, page 2362
Ht: 7′5″ Wd: 41½″ Dp: 21½″

ownsend Chest-on-Chests

P-5894 & P-6309: Rare matched pair of Chippendale mahogany bonnet top chest-on-chests. Goddard-Townsend. Newport, Rhode Island, circa 1760-1770. Despite minor construction differences the chests are apparent companions. Both have the original pine tree brasses, flame finials with fluted bowls and compatable wood grain patterns of mottled and plum pudding mahogany. To our knowledge this is the only pair of Goddard-Townsend chest-on-chests known.

P-6309: Descended in the family of George Gibbs II, wealthy shipping merchant. Newport, Rhode Island
Ht: 7′5″ Wd: 41½″ Dp: 21½″

P-6271: Sheraton mahogany sofa with bowed crest and seat frame. The arm term nals are faced with crosshatched checkered inlay with bulbous reeded arm support The delicate legs are reeded and sharply tapered. Salem, Massachusetts, circ 1800-1810.

Ht: 36 3/8″ Lg: 77¼″ Dp: 24″

P-4371: Leather fire bucket depicting a spread eagle and banner inscribed "Jefferson Fire Society," John M. Fiske 1826. Charlestown (Mass.) Accompanying the bucket is the register of the Society with John M. Fisk(e) listed as member #32.

Ht: 19″ Diam: 8 1/2″

Ex-collection Charles K. Davis
Illustrated in Sack "Opportunities in American Antiques" Brochure 29 and recently reacquired.

P-6217: Pair of Sheraton mahogany side chairs. The solid urn shaped splat with carved drapery supports a three feathered plume, flanked by fan carved spandrels. Philadelphia, circa 1800-1810.

Ht: 36″

A chair of this design is illustrated in Montgomery's "American Furniture, The Federal Period" plate 98.

P-6308: Chippendale mahogany bonnet top block front chest-on-chest. Engaged fluted pilasters flank the upper case of beaded graduated drawers, the center one of which is enhanced by a deeply carved fan. The lower case is comprised of four beaded graduated blocked drawers and rests on blocked bracket feet. Original urn and flame finials and pine tree brasses. Richly figured mahogany of fine grain and color. Massachusetts, circa 1770-1780.

Ht: 6′ 6″ Wd: 44″ Dp: 24″

P-6005: Chippendale mahogany pembroke table, bowed front and frame with serpentine drop leaves. The bowed frame contains a drawer in one end. The square molded legs with pierced corner brackets support flat cross stretchers with spade cut-out. Mellow patina. Portsmouth, New Hampshire, circa 1770-1790.

Ht: 28½″ Lg: 31¾″ Wd: 36½″ (open) 20¼″ (closed)

P-6004: Hepplewhite mahogany serving table or hall table of rare small size. The case has a bowed front with serpentine sides. The bowed frame is fronted by a birds-eye maple drawer. The top centers a dark and light fan inlaid patera. Line inlaid tapered legs. New Hampshire, circa 1790-1810.

Ht: 33 1/4″ Wd: 28 1/2″ Dp: 16 1/4″

P-6060: Chippendale mahogany pembroke table. The square legs are connected by flat cross stretchers with spade cutout, one drawer with original chased bail brass, pierced corner brackets, fine bronze patina. Philadelphia, circa 1760-1780. Tables of this general form were also fashioned in New York and Newport.

Ht: 28¾″ Wd. open: 37½″ Wd. closed: 22″ Lg: 29″

P-6049: Chippendale walnut straight front bureau of rare small size. The four graduated drawers have molded edges as does the overhanging top. The case is supported on spurred bracket feet. The size, fine proportions, mellow old patina and original brasses combine to make this an exceptional example of this form. Pennsylvania, circa 1780.

Ht: 32½″ Wd: 35½″ Dp: 19¾″

P-6300: Hepplewhite mahogany grandmother or half-high clock. The moon phase dial with striking mechanism and three auxiliary dials is a rare and probably unique feature. The dials indicate seconds, days of the week and day of the month, as well as an alarm. The dial is inscribed "Joshua Wilder, Hingham." The case exhibits fine craftsmanship with crossbanded borders and original fretwork. Made by Joshua Wilder for David Whiton of Hingham, Massachusetts, circa 1810-1820.

Ht: 48″ Wd: 11 1/2″ Dp: 6 1/8″

Aaron Willard's Masterpiece

2612

P-6299: This supreme banjo clock is documented as the work of Aaron Willard by the die-stamp on the brass movement which reads "A. Willard, Boston 1808." Additionally, the lower eglomise tablet is signed on the reverse "Willard and Nolen, Washington Street, Boston." The front of the tablet depicts and is inscribed "Hercules Assisting Atlas in Supporting the Globe". The sides of the case are painted white indicating its original purpose as a bridal clock. The carved and gilded floral side brackets are, to our knowledge, unique. Made by Aaron Willard, Boston, Massachusetts 1808.

Ex-collection Dexter Spalding
Exhibited in Museum of Fine Arts, Boston
Illustrated in "In Praise of America" by Wendy Cooper, page 23.

Ht: 45" Wd: 10 1/4"

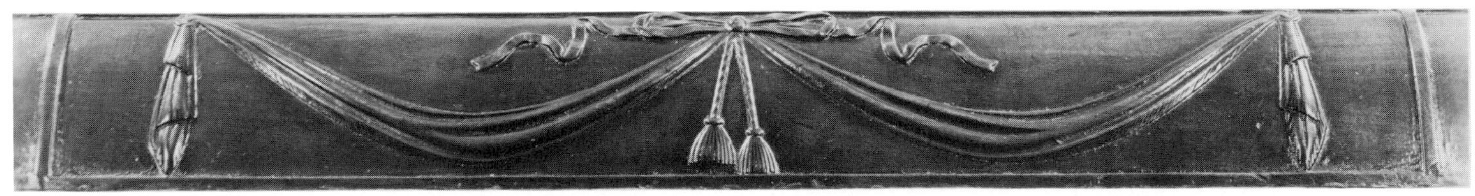

P-5411: Sheraton mahogany sofa with three panel carved back, slender reeded legs ending in bulbous feet with brass casters, mellow brown patina. Made by Duncan Phyfe or a contemporary of equal rank. New York, circa 1800-1810.

Ht: 37″ Wd: 78″ Dp: 30″

P-6288: Pastel portrait of Joseph Stretch by the "New Jersey Artist." The pastel is in the original gilded frame and eglomise glass mat with octagonal gilded border and leaf spandrels. Circa 1805-1815.

Ht: 37″ Wd: 30 5/8″

A scholarly treatise on the New Jersey artist and geneological data on Joseph Stretch, prepared by Carl Williams is available to the purchaser. More than thirty pastel portraits, all of New Jersey residents, are identified as by this artist.

Joseph Stretch, Burlington County, New Jersey (1785-1815) was the son of Peter Stretch II, of the Philadelphia clockmaking family.

P-6295: Octagonal tin tray with maritime scene inscribed "Ship Hazard, 1799. Built by Retire Becket." The scene depicts a fully rigged three masted frigate flying an American naval flag. The ship was originally owned by John and Richard Gardner of Salem, Massachustts — 1799.

Ht: 18¾″ Wd: 14 3/8″

P-4343: Sheraton mahogany armchair, the crest panel with ribbon and bowknot and sheaf of wheat carving, double cross bar splats with rosette carved centers, bell shaped seat with reeded facade, old or original finish. Attributed to Duncan Phyfe, New York, circa 1800-1810.

Ex-collection Charles K. Davis
Illustrated in ''American Antiques from Israel Sack Collection'' The Davis Collection, Vol. V, pg. 1346.

Ht: 32¼″ Wd: 21½″

P-6171: Empire mahogany work table. The end box compartments each front simulated drawers and demilune tambours. The hinged top reveals a writing compartment. The case is supported by bulbous turned acanthus carved columns and acanthus carved legs and connecting stretcher. New York, circa 1815-1825.

Ht: 30 1/2″ Wd: 27 3/4″ Dp: 16 3/4″

P-1110: Sheraton mahogany tambour work table. The tambour center fronts a deep drawer; the top has finely figured crotch grain and is hinged to reveal a fitted compartment. The base has an urn column and molded legs ending in carved paw feet. Made by Duncan Phyfe or a contemporary of equal rank. New York, circa 1810-1820.

Ht: 29 1/2″ top: 25″ × 12 3/4″

Ex-collection: Charles Hallam Keep

A Seymour Classic

P-6237: Sheraton painted and decorated sewing table. This table represents one of the supreme pieces of American decorated furniture from the standpoint of stature and state of preservation. The table is related to a group of sewing tables by characteristics such as superior structural craftsmanship, a complex inlaid or painted top and aprons, and a side opening sewing bag with locking feature identified as the work of John and Thomas Seymour. The painting is the work of a highly skilled artist and is attributed to John Rizzo Penniman on the basis of a related vignette signed by Penniman. The table retains the original lion's ring brasses. The bottom drawer is fitted with compartments retaining their rare covered lids of tooled red leather. The lunettes, blistered pattern top border and pilasters are painted to simulate inlay. Made by John and Thomas Seymour with top painting attributed to John R. Penniman. Boston, Massachusetts, circa 1800-1810. Illustrated ''Supplement to John & Thomas Seymour'' Stoneman. Cover, frontispiece and pages 72 & 73. Illustrated ''American Painted Furniture'' Dean A. Fales, Jr., page 115.

Ht: 30″ Wd: 20″ Dp: 15 1/2″

P-6228: Classical pianoforte signed by Gibson & Davis, New York. The case is formed of finely grained mahogany veneer delineated by cross-grained borders. It rests on two pedestals with outsplayed saber legs connected by a medial stretcher, all of which are beautifully carved with reeding and acanthus motifs of the character and quality associated with Duncan Phyfe to whom the case is attributed. The legs terminate in brass paw feet on raised castors. The original pedal remains intact. An almost identical piano is in the collection of the Metropolitan Museum, New York. Circa 1815-1822.

See: McClelland ''Duncan Phyfe and The English Regency'' page 86.

Ht: 36 3/4″ Lg: 70″ Dp: 25 1/4″

P-6119: Hepplewhite mahogany inlaid card table, straight front with ovolu corners, oval center panel in mitred curly maple frame, tapered legs with arrow tapered feet. Mellow light brown patina. Massachusetts, circa 1780-1800.

Ht: 28 1/2″ Wd: 36″ Dp: 34″

P-6017: Hepplewhite mahogany three part dining table. The table contains two demilune console ends each with a drop leaf and a drop leaf center section. The aprons have crossbanded inlaid borders and the tapered legs have crossbanded inlaid cuffs. The tops exhibit fine figured grain, mellow light brown patina. Massachusetts, circa 1790-1800.

Ht: 28 3/4″ Lg: 104″ Wd: 47 7/8″

P5732: Chippendale mahogany side table. One drawer with original brass handle. Boldly overhanging top with strong crotch figured grain. Square stop fluted legs. Satin patina. Townsend school. Newport, Rhode Island, circa 1760-1780.

Ht: 26¾″ Wd: 32¼″ Dp: 22¼″

A Century of Standards

Some people view 1990 as the first year of the last decade of the 20th century. We view 1990 as the first year of the decade that leads us into the 21st century.

This inaugural decade offers many opportunities for collectors just as did the inaugural decade of the 1890's. It was then that many great collections, several of which now form the nuclei of major museum collections, were beginning to be assembled.

Such remarkable opportunity is exemplified by the japanned William and Mary high chest illustrated in this brochure. The reacquisition of this great rarity demonstrates our ability and interest in acquiring superior pieces to offer to new and future collectors.

Additionally, we have included more than a dozen objects, such as the Newport table on the page opposite, which we have previously owned and recently repurchased. In always aspiring to own and offer objects of connoisseur level, it is a pleasure to have the opportunity to reaffirm our confidence in the quality of pieces that our firm has selected in the past by reacquiring them.

At the outset of the current century Israel Sack saw and appreciated the inherent beauty of furniture made by our Colonial craftsmen. Aesthetic merit, authenticity and quality of craftsmanship became the standards for the selection of objects for his clients. Throughout the ensuing century this focus has remained the firm's preeminent objective.

Today, as we work with clients, many of those choices will build the great collections of the 21st century, our decision-making process remains consistent. We critically evaluate objects currently available and purchase only those which we believe meet the criteria set forth at the firm's inception. Our emphasis has never concentrated on the speculative aspects of collecting, but rather on offering value based on merit. We attempt to benefit our customers by passing on both our many years of experience and the results of our constant research.

Our sense of responsibility to you, combined with our sincere dedication to the achievements of America's artisans, demand that we search out and present the best of their creations.

In an effort to make these selections available to you, our clients, as soon as possible, we are producing our brochures on a more frequent basis.

These brochures have documented thousands of items in the 33 years of their publications. In this, our 47th brochure, and those upcoming, we will continue to illustrate fine objects reflecting the choice individual expression of craftsmanship that has stood the test of time.

Albert M. Sack — Harold Sack — Robert M. Sack

Deanne Levison Consultant

P563: Rare Hepplewhite mahogany inlaid small sideboard with wavy gallery, the case has a central cupboard deep drawer flanked by end compartments with drop fronts hinged by brass quadrants. The oval sunbursts with checkered inlaid borders are in mitered backgrounds. The inlaid sunbursts are repeated on the sides; tapered legs ending in spade feet. Magnificent mellow brown patina. Attributed to Stephen Badlam, Boston, Massachusetts, circa 1780-1800.

The attribution to Badlam is based on the relationship to a branded Badlam oval tray with related wavy gallery and inlaid sunburst in checkered inlaid border (Benj. Flayderman Sale #82, 1931).

Ht: 39″ Wd: 60″ Dp: 23½″

P156: Pair of Hepplewhite inlaid card tables, rectangular frames with curly satinwood veneer flanked by inlaid rosette paterae. The line inlaid legs are tapered ending in spade feet. One table has a drawer in one end, the other a drawer in each end. The tops have molded edges. Maryland, circa 1780-1800.

Ht: 30″ Wd: 33¾″ Dp: 16½″

P6318: Sheraton mahogany four post bed, acanthus carved and reeded foot-posts, in the finest original state of preservation including the rails, head-board, tester frame and finish. Salem, Massachusetts circa 1800-1810. The rare width of 64¼″ approaches king size.

Ht: 93½″ Wd: 64¼″ Lg: 76½″

P6323: Chippendale mahogany block and shell tall clock. The boldly blocked door panel features a finely carved shell in the Goddard-Townsend tradition. The brass dial with engraved spandrels bears the plaque Edward Spalding, Providence. The case is Newport, circa 1770-1780.

Ht: 7′7″ Wd: 21½″ Dp: 9¼″

P4581: Chippendale walnut tall clock with inlaid decoration. The case qualifies as a masterpiece of Pennsylvania German art. The center of the fan carved waist door and the escutcheon of the dial door are ivory. The original brass dial with engraved spandrels and seascape is engraved Benj. Morris, New Britain. The brass movement is replaced and the rocking ship of the seascape was removed. The case has a choice warm light brown patina. Made by Benjamin Morris, New Britain, Bucks County, Pennsylvania, dated 1787.

Ht: 94½″ Wd: 17″ Dp: 10″

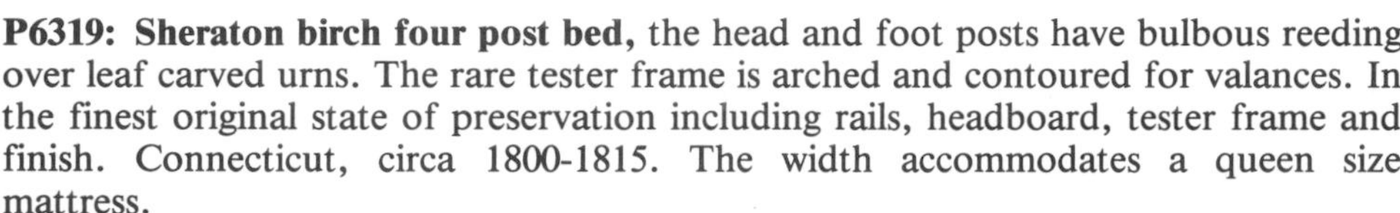

P6319: Sheraton birch four post bed, the head and foot posts have bulbous reeding over leaf carved urns. The rare tester frame is arched and contoured for valances. In the finest original state of preservation including rails, headboard, tester frame and finish. Connecticut, circa 1800-1815. The width accommodates a queen size mattress.

Ht: 95½″ Wd: 59½″ Lg: 81½″

P3391: Chippendale San Domingan mahogany block front kneehole desk or bureau table with arched panelled center door and narrow drawer above. The compact scale and bold round blocking accentuated by the original large brasses create the effect of power and virility for which the block front school is famous. The superb close grained mahogany from which the piece was fashioned has acquired a beautiful mellow brown patina. The Queen Anne influence is apparent in the small scale and semi-circular blocking. Boston or Salem, Massachusetts, circa 1750-1760.

Ht: 29¾″ Wd: 34″ Dp: 21″

P6337: Set of six Chippendale mahogany claw and ball foot side chairs with carved trefoil pierced splats and leaf carved crest rails. The front seat rails are centered by cartouche carving flanked by beaded arches. Mellow light brown patina. The slip seat frames are numbered I to VI corresponding with numbers inscribed inside the seat rails. Philadelphia, circa 1760-1780.

Ht: 37¾″

Ex-collection Mrs. John H. Easby

Illustrated Horner's "Blue Book of Philadelphia Furniture", plate 358

P4051: Queen Anne walnut wing chair. The chair is a fine example of the favorite form of Massachusetts wing chairs in the Queen Anne influence. The chamfered rear legs have a one inch extension. Massachusetts, circa 1740-1760.

Ht: 46½″ Wd: 34½″

P932: Queen Anne mahogany tea table with slides, finely scalloped apron, cabriole legs with platformed pad feet, and a fine light brown patina. Massachusetts circa 1740-1760. One of the rarest and most sought after forms of American tea tables, this piece shows exceptional vitality in its design and execution.

Descended in the Dewart family.

Ht: 27½″ Top: Lg. 30½″ Wd. 18½″

P6313: Chippendale mahogany and gilt mirror with finely scrolled crest and base, gilt phoenix silhouetted in crest, original mirror glass and backboard. American or English, circa 1760-1780.

Ht: 40″ Wd: 17″

P2952: Queen Anne walnut side chair with boldly carved Newport shell in crest, wavy stiles, balloon seat, shell and floral carved knees. Newport, Rhode Island, circa 1740-1760.

Ht: 37¼″

P811: Chippendale mahogany block front chest-on-chest with broken arch top and carved rosettes. The upper case has a fan carved center drawer flanked by fluted pilasters. The bracket feet have cyma scrolled inner outlines and the center pendant has a spurred center arc. The piece is distinguished by bold blocking, original pine tree brasses and a choice bronze patina. Massachusetts, circa 1760-1780. Descended in the Greenhalge family.

Ht: 7′4″ Wd: 42″ Dp: 21″

P2486: William and Mary cherry side chair with carved crest, cane back and seat, scrolled apron, turned legs ending in Spanish feet. Massachusetts, circa 1710-1730.

This chair belonged to Colonel John Stoddard (1682-1748) of Northampton, Massachusetts. It was exhibited in the Harvard Tercentenary Exhibit, 1936 #216 in the Catalogue.

Inventory of John Stoddard's estate Dec. 1748 lists ''nine cain chairs 34^{S}.

Ht: 45½″

A Boston Japanned Masterpiece

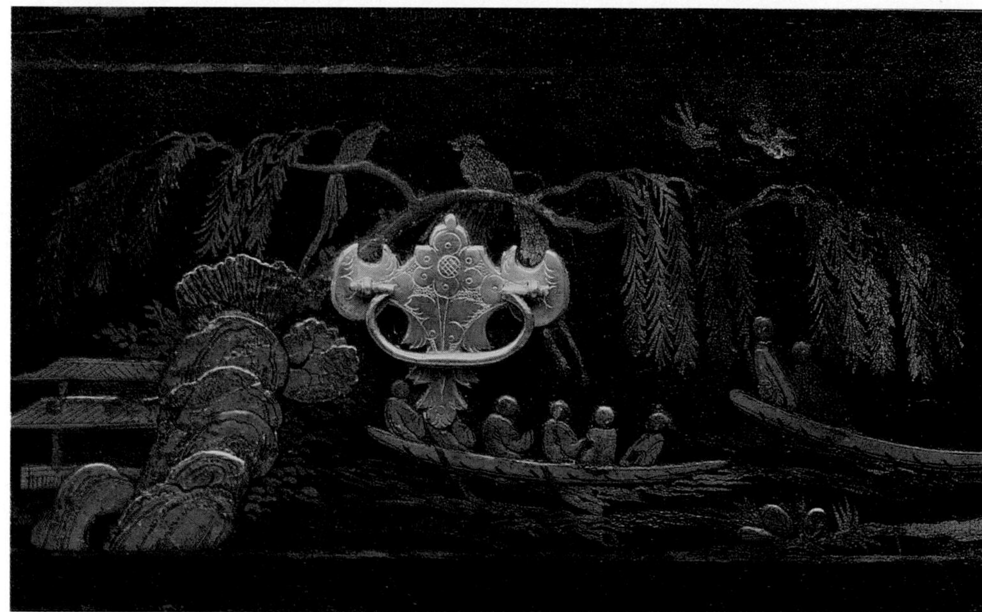

P4222: William and Mary maple and white pine high chest of drawers with the original japanned decoration, made and signed by John Scottow, Boston, Massachusetts circa 1725-1735 with japanned decoration attributed to Robert Davis, Boston, Massachusetts circa 1725-1735.

The art of japanning, influenced by pattern books and techniques from the Orient became popular in England during the last quarter of the 17th century and the first half of the 18th century. The art traveled to the Colonies centering mainly in Boston where several japanners plied the trade. American examples are quite rare. In our eighty-five years in this field we have owned but three japanned pieces, of which this is one.

Six or seven William and Mary high chests are known. Others can be seen in the collections of the Metropolitan Museum, The Winterthur Museum, Historic Deerfield and the Adams National Historic Site, Quincy, Massachusetts.

This example is in superb original state. The raised decoration of Oriental figures on the drawers is virtually intact as is the decoration on the faceted legs, stretchers, ball feet and sides. The drawers retain the original engraved brasses which are secured by cotter pins and never disturbed. Each drawer is signed SCOTTOW. Robert Davis, Boston Japanner (d 1739) worked in the trade with his father-in-law, William Randall (working 1715-1735).

Descended in the Cogswell-Dixon family.

Ht: 64¼″ Wd: 40¾″ Dp: 22½″

Ex-collection:
Linda H. & George M. Kaufman

Exhibited:
The National Gallery of Art, Washington, D.C., 1986
The Cooper-Hewitt Museum, New York City, 1988
The Carnegie Institute, Pittsburgh, PA, 1989

Illustrated:
"American Furniture from the Kaufman Collection"
Pl. 17, pgs. 50, 51, 52 & 53.
"Courts and Colonies," Exhibition at
Cooper Hewitt Museum No. 174, pg. 204 & 205, pl. 174.

P4164: Hepplewhite mahogany mirror of important size with original eglomise glass panel depicting a landscape scene; the swan's neck pediment has carved and gilded moldings ending in carved rosettes and centered by a beautiful original gilded urn with sprays of flowers and wheat; the scrollboard is centered by an oval inlaid shell patera; the mirror glass and back are the originals as is the gilding. New York, circa 1780-1810.

Illustrated ANTIQUES "The Robb Collection" Frontispiece April 1968.

Ht: 65″ Wd: 23″

Ex-collection: Mr. & Mrs. Walter B. Robb

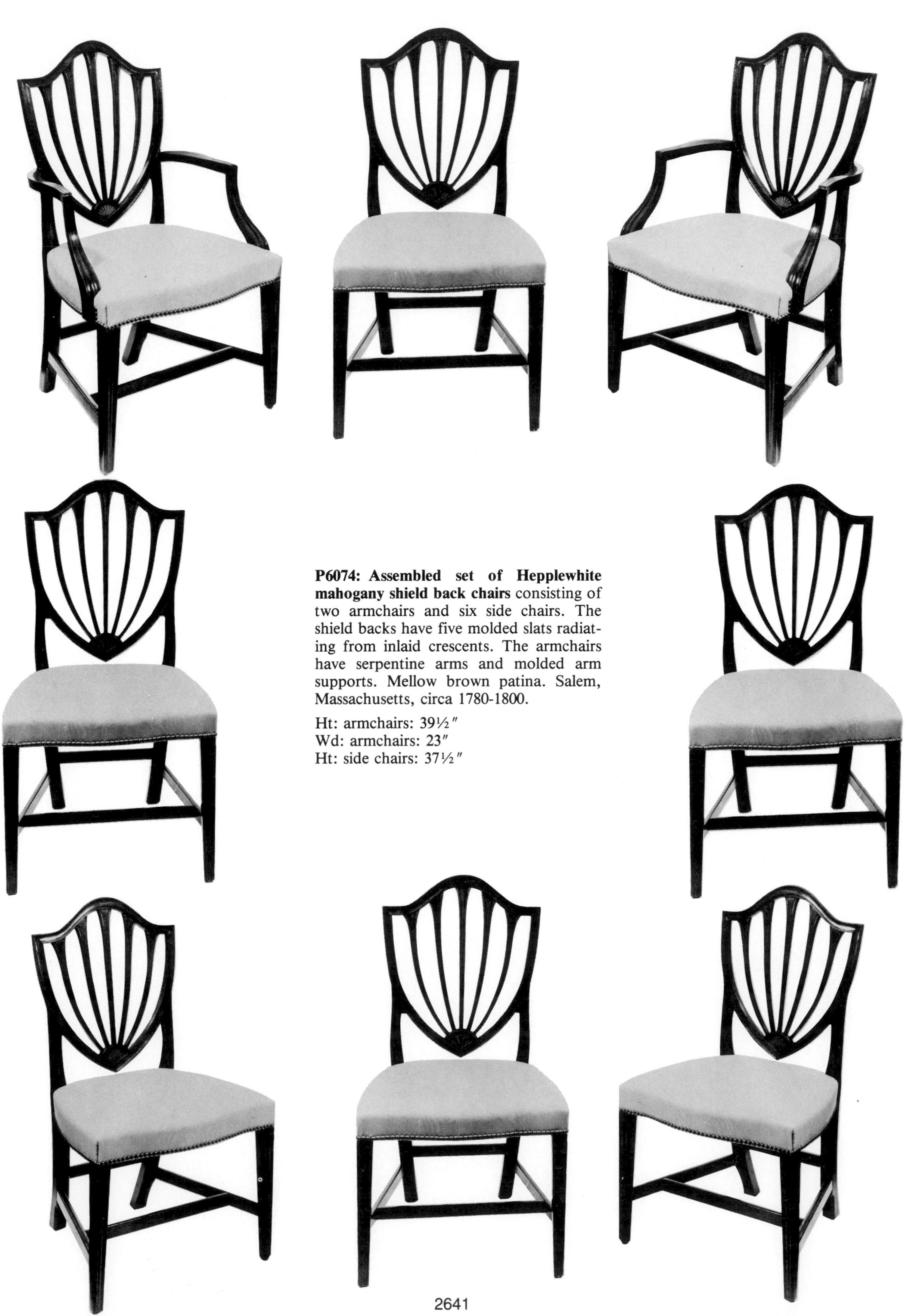

P6074: Assembled set of Hepplewhite mahogany shield back chairs consisting of two armchairs and six side chairs. The shield backs have five molded slats radiating from inlaid crescents. The armchairs have serpentine arms and molded arm supports. Mellow brown patina. Salem, Massachusetts, circa 1780-1800.

Ht: armchairs: 39½″
Wd: armchairs: 23″
Ht: side chairs: 37½″

P6338: Pair of Queen Anne walnut side chairs with balloon seats, vase shaped splats and original slip seat frames. Rhode Island, circa 1740-1760.

Ht: 40½″

P867: Queen Anne cherry porringer top tea table with drawer; graceful cabriole legs and scrolled apron. Fine amber color. A rare and successful form. It is the first example we have encountered. Massachusetts or Rhode Island, circa 1740-1760.

Ht: 26½″ Lg: 32½″ Wd: 24″

P6335: Sheraton mahogany sofa with incurvate reeded arms and reeded seat frame. The three panelled carved back features a center panel of ribbon and sheaf of wheat, the end panels ribbon and wheat stalks, reeded legs ending in bulbous feet. The sofa is branded by the maker Michael Allison, New York circa 1800-1810. This rare documented example advances our knowledge of a worthy competitor of Duncan Phyfe.

Ht: 36″ Wd: 80½″ Dp: 25¼″

P6312: Classical mahogany lyre base card table. The frame has canted corners and is centered by a drapery carved panel; the frame is supported by twin lyres. The acanthus carving is on the side edges of the lyres as well as the front; the carving extends on the graceful outsplayed legs, attributed to Michael Allison. New York, circa 1810-1820.

The attribution to Allison is based on a related drapery panel on a Sheraton card table by Michael Allison (''Antiques'' September 1946, pg. 179).

Ht: 31¼″ Wd: 36″ Dp: 17½″

P6302: Classical gilt convex mirror with candle brackets. The coved frame with carved inner border and spheres is crested by a mythical sea horse flanked by dolphins, American or English, circa 1800-1815.

Ht: 34″ Wd: 21″

P6201: Hepplewhite mahogany Martha Washington armchair or lolling chair, serpentine crest, molded arm supports and tapered legs. Massachusetts, circa 1780-1790.

Ht: 45″ Wd: 25¼″

P6305: Rare brass mantle clock with standing figure of General George Washington with a sword in one hand and the Treaty of Alliance in the other. The Declaration of Independence is on a simulated desk surmounted by eagle standard. A rare or unique interpretation within the group of Washington clocks imported from France into the port of Baltimore, circa 1790-1810. The historic documents depicted suggest an early date.

Ht: 14½″ Wd: 9″

P6334: Hepplewhite mahogany Martha Washington armchair or lolling chair, the molding of the arms extends to the back and continues on the arm support, serpentine crest and seat frame, plain tapered legs. Salem, Massachusetts, circa 1780-1800. The view of the frame shows the original triangular blocks.

Ht: 43″ Wd: 22¼″

P6322: Chippendale maple chest-on-chest of small scale and pleasing proportions. Mellow old or original patina and retaining the important original willow brasses. Massachusetts, circa 1760-1780.

Ht: 73¾″ Wd: 39¾″ Dp: 18¾″

P2387: Queen Anne walnut corner chair, horseshoe shaped seat with cabriole front leg, turned cross stretchers, vase shaped splats, and mellow light brown patina. Massachusetts or Rhode Island, circa 1740-1760.

Ht: 30½″ Wd: 24″

P6336: Rare pair of Connecticut comb-back Windsor armchairs. The flaring upswept ears of the serpentine crest are echoed in the shape of the handholds. The finely defined saddle seats and baluster turnings, the strong outward splay of the legs and the retention of old red paint beneath later paint makes this a most desirable pair. Connecticut, circa 1780-1800.

Ht: 37½″ Wd: 15½″

P409: Queen Anne mahogany bonnet top highboy of rare low height. Evidently made to accommodate a low ceiling, it has finely modelled cabriole legs ending in platformed pad feet. The piece retains a mellow light brown patina, as well as the original brasses. Boston or Salem, Massachusetts, circa 1750-1770.

Ht: 6′8″ Wd: 41½″ Dp: 20¾″

P6321: Hepplewhite mahogany shield back side chair, the splat with elliptical reeded urn and carved drapery in oval frame, plain tapered legs. Providence or Newport, Rhode Island, circa 1780-1800.

Ht: 40″

P6316: Sheraton mahogany serving table. The rectangular case has two rows of drawers with richly figured veneered fronts. The drawers are flanked by reeded turrets supported on spiral columns with leaf carved capitals. The bulbous feet and brass casters both have leaf carving. New York, circa 1800-1815.

Ht: 39″ Wd: 36″ Dp: 19″

P6310: Hepplewhite mahogany inlaid mantle clock, with ogee bracket feet, kidney dial, replaced fretwork, made and inscribed by Aaron Willard. Boston, Massachusetts, circa 1800-1810.

Ht: 35½″ Wd: 13¾″ Dp: 6″

P6325: Parian ware standing figure of George Washington in toga holding a scroll. On circular base inscribed WASHINGTON, American, 19th century.

Ht: 13½″

P6004: Sheraton mahogany bowfront bureau with turret corners, the drawers flanked by two reeded turret columns with leaf carved capitals in star punch background. The top has concentric ringed border. Reeded legs ending in bulbous feet. Choice bronze color. Attributed to William Hook. Salem, Massachusetts, circa 1800-1810.

Ht: 42″ Wd: 48½″ Dp: 22″

P3724: Pair of watercolor coats of arms of the Lincoln and Sullivan families in the original frames. John Coles of Charlestown, Massachusetts circa 1800-1810.

The Lincoln coat of arms is for the Hingham branch of the Lincoln family, ancestors of Abraham Lincoln. The depiction of the American flag with 13 stars is rare.

The Sullivan arms are for James Sullivan, delegate to the Continental Congress and later Governor of Massachusetts.

An informative biographical account of the Lincoln-Sullivan families accompanies the watercolors.

Ht: 15½″ Wd: 11½″

P6233: Curly maple tea caddy with inlaid border and warm patina. The interior is fitted with three compartments with sliding inlaid covers. New England, circa 1790-1810.

Ht: 6″ Wd: 9½″ Dp: 5½″

P6317: Oil painting of maritime scene inscribed "Gen'l Warren of Fairhaven, J. Graham Master passing the Serrallio Point of Constantinopoli 1831". The scene depicts a fine view of Constantinople with two ships flying the American flag. Probably by an Italian Painter (possibly Corsini) 1831.

Ht: 28″ Wd: 36″

P6320: Oval tin decorated tray depicting a young lady with a broad brimmed hat. American or English, circa 1800-1810.

Lg: 21″ Wd: 16″

1991 and Beyond

The ups and downs of economic cycles is nothing new. We seem to have in our century either an excess of pessimism or an excess of optimism. Through it all, the knowledgeable collector and dealer rides through the waves and steadfastly adheres to the time-proven principle that great art continues to seek and maintain its own level.

As in the seventies, the beginning years of the decade of the eighties were times not unlike those we are presently experiencing. It was a time of caution and questioning in all markets, and yet the eighties, like the seventies, brought new appreciation, enlarged numbers of collectors and resultant higher prices than had ever occurred in the past. In the beginning decade of the nineties neither the levels of understanding and appreciation of high quality objects nor the numbers of new or seasoned collectors has decreased. Perhaps the developments of the previous decades should serve as a guide for anticipating the future of fine American antique furniture. The price levels of the late 1980's proved the early 1980's to be a time of opportunity. Obviously many found sound advice, as well as good buys. These examples could be the best indicators of the future a collector could have.

Through the years our faith in the market for fine authentic American antiques continues to be evidenced by our aggressive buying. During the past several months we have been fortunate to repurchase a number of items sold by us in previous years, and over twenty such items are offered in this brochure. The good will we have maintained with clients has afforded us the opportunity to reacquire these choice items. We try to maintain a healthy balance so that our prices reflect not only quality, but also the realities of the market place.

We invite further inquiries regarding the wide variety of outstanding objects offered in this brochure to you, our old clients. To new converts to Americana of the 1990's, we extend a cordial welcome to our gallery to become acquainted.

Albert M. Sack   Harold Sack   Robert M. Sack

Deanne Levison Consultant

P-784: William and Mary walnut lowboy. The cockbeaded case has dovetailed construction, and the three separated drawers, which are hallmarks of Pennsylvania lowboys, are each surrounded on the base and sides by double beaded molding. The serpentine flat shaped stretchers intersect on a serrated platform which is centered by the original turned upright finial. Pennsylvania, circa 1710-1730.

Ht: 28¼″ Wd: 34½″ Dp: 20½″

This is one of an extremely small group of Pennsylvania lowboys to survive from this period.

Illustrated "American Antiques from Israel Sack Collection" Vol. I, pg. 162 and recently repurchased.

P-6358: Early decorated Taunton blanket chest with decorations of tulips, vines and birds and dated 1732. The decoration of creamy white and vermillion is remarkably brilliant. Attributed to Robert Crosman, Taunton, Massachusetts, 1732.

Purchased by us from a direct descendant.

Ht: 32½″ Wd: 38″ Dp: 17¾″

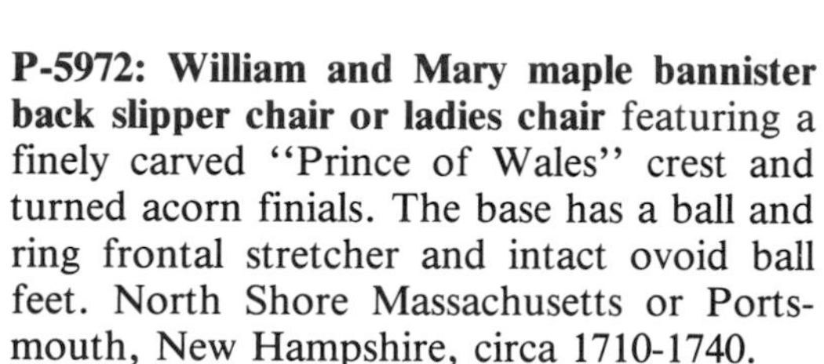

P-5972: William and Mary maple bannister back slipper chair or ladies chair featuring a finely carved ''Prince of Wales'' crest and turned acorn finials. The base has a ball and ring frontal stretcher and intact ovoid ball feet. North Shore Massachusetts or Portsmouth, New Hampshire, circa 1710-1740.

Ht: 41″

Ex-collection Israel Sack, Inc. and recently repurchased.

P-6368: Early maple slat back high chair, the back has four serpentine slats graduated in size, nicely modelled arms, outsplayed legs retaining the original ball feet, old reddish brown paint. Delaware Valley, circa 1740-1770. The foot rest is an old addition.

Ht: 39¼″

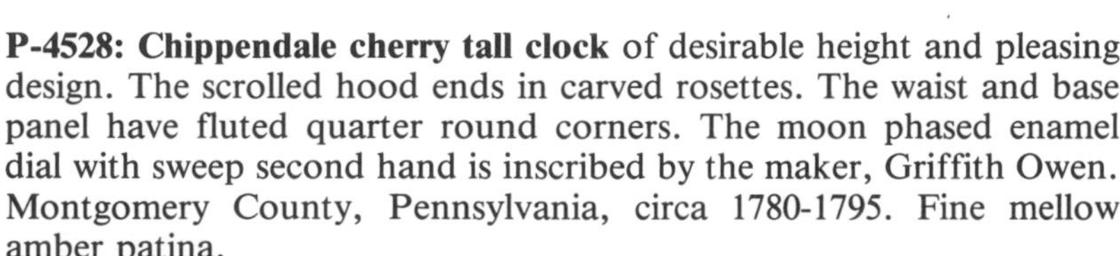

P-4528: Chippendale cherry tall clock of desirable height and pleasing design. The scrolled hood ends in carved rosettes. The waist and base panel have fluted quarter round corners. The moon phased enamel dial with sweep second hand is inscribed by the maker, Griffith Owen. Montgomery County, Pennsylvania, circa 1780-1795. Fine mellow amber patina.

Ht: 7′ 5¾″ Wd: 20½″ Dp: 1¼″

Illustrated in "American Antiques from Israel Sack Collection" Vol. VI, pg. 1443 and recently repurchased.

P-6381: Sheraton mahogany four post bed with finely carved foot posts and rare original tester frame. The turrett corners of the frame are acanthus leaf carved and the front and sides have veneered panels. The posts are carved with acanthus leaf, reeded collars and beaded dividers. Original rails and headboard. Salem, Massachusetts, circa 1800-1815.

Ht: 88″ Wd: 58″ Lg: 76¾″

P-780: Sheraton mahogany four post bed. The foot posts are finely carved with acanthus leaf and flowers with reeded collars and beaded dividers. The rails and headboard are original. Salem, Massachusetts, circa 1800-1815.

Ht: 87¾″ Wd: 58″ Lg: 76½″

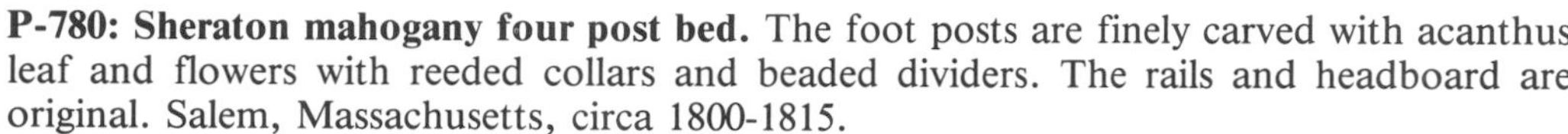

Illustrated in "American Antiques from Israel Sack Collection" Vol. I, pg. 182 and recently repurchased.

This bed and the one on the page across were obviously carved by the same masterful hand and would form rare companions.

P-6359: Rare small Chippendale camelback settee. The graceful form of the top rail, the scrolled arm rests and the molded front legs with rectangular connecting stretchers to the rear legs add to the successful design of this desirable form. Massachusetts circa 1770-1780.

Ht: 37″ Wd: 52″ Dp: 26″

P-6355: Chippendale mahogany claw and ball foot side chair. The magnificent form and carving place this in the first rank of Philadelphia chairmaking. The crest rail is particularly outstanding with a shell carved center from which emanates scroll and fringe carving terminating in shell carved ears. The finely carved splat is also seen on a few models of Queen Anne formation. The chair is in a fine state of preservation. Philadelphia, circa 1760-1780.

Ht: 39″

Illustrated in Hornor's ''Blue Book of Philadelphia Furniture'' plate 327.

P-4028: Queen Anne cherry bonnet top highboy. The slender bandy cabriole legs form a graceful silhouette with the cyma shaped apron with its cupid's bow center. The carved fan of the lower case and the carved sunburst of the upper case have deeply scribed outlines. The small batwing brasses are original, the flame finials are old replacements. The small scale adds to the appeal of this exceptional model. Hartford, Connecticut, circa 1765-1785.

Ht: 7′ 2″ Wd: 38½″ Dp: 20″

Ex-collection: Philip Young, pioneer Boston collector

Illustrated in "American Antiques from Israel Sack Collection" Vol. V, pg. 1138 and recently repurchased.

P-6378: Fine set of six Queen Anne maple side chairs. The yoke crests surmount serpentine vase splats and stiles. The seat frames are arched along the lower edge of the sides and scalloped across the fronts. The well formed cabriole front legs terminate in raised pad feet and are connected to the chamfered rear stiles by block and turned stretchers. They are additionally enhanced by a warm mellow color and patina. Massachusetts, circa 1750-1770.

Ht: 41″

Ex-collection Israel Sack, Inc. and recently repurchased.

P-6395: Chippendale mahogany oxbow bureau with blocked ends and ogee bracket feet. The piece shows the handiwork of a superior artisan and is distinguished by bold blocking and exceptional selections of figured grain. The top and sides have mottled mahogany striping. The drawer fronts have a wavy grain and retain the original brasses, except two. The molded edged top has notched corners. Massachusetts, circa 1760-1780.

Ht: 33½″ Wd: 37½″ Dp: 21½″

P-6371: Rare pair of Queen Anne walnut and gilt mirrors. The crests feature attractive scroll and cutout outlines with gilt cartouche ornaments repeated in modified form on base, original glass. Continental for the American market, circa 1740-1760. This type of imported mirror frequented Colonial homes but is seldom found in pairs.

Ht: 30″ Wd: 13″

P-6366: Queen Anne walnut sconce mirror with scrolled crest and base. The original sconce backplate supports an old, but adapted, candle bracket. English, circa 1740-1760.

Ht: 29″ Wd: 9¾″

P-6349: Queen Anne walnut small mirror with nicely scrolled crest, mellow patina and original glass. American or English, circa 1740-1760.

Ht: 24″ Wd: 12″

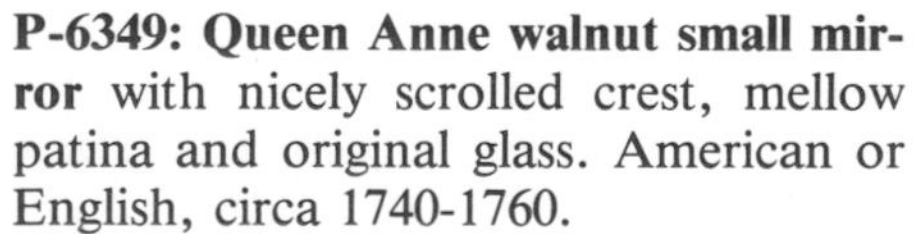

P-6394: San Domingan mahogany tall case clock with brass spandrelled dial inscribed by Simon Willard, Roxbury (Massachusetts). The case, of typical Willard school formation exhibits superior craftsmanship, selection of finely figured mahogany and exceptional detailing of a quality rarely equalled, even by the master. The clock is in superb original condition, retaining the original carved and gilded flame finials and pierced fretwork. Made and signed by Simon Willard, Roxbury, Massachusetts, circa 1780-1785.

Ht: 7′ 10″ Wd: 13½″ Dp: 9½″

Line of descent:

1. Nathaniel Bradlee (1746-1813) Housewright and manufacturer of cisterns. Nathaniel Bradlee built his house at 36 Hollis Street, Boston, in 1771. In this house certain Sons of Liberty, including Nathaniel Bradlee, dressed as Indians to participate in the Boston Tea Party, 1773.

2. Elizabeth Bradlee (1781-1869) married Noah Doggett Sept. 15, 1810. Elizabeth and Noah Doggett bought out heirs of 36 Hollis Street (Boston Tea Party House) and moved there in 1823. The Simon Willard clock remained in the house.

3. Nathaniel Bradlee Doggett (1818-   ).

4. Brewster D. Doggett of Wiscasset, Maine, most recent family owner. This clock was loaned by Brewster Doggett to the Museum of Fine Arts, Boston, in 1939. It was on exhibition there 1939-1960.

2671

P-6367: Chippendale mahogany small cabinet. The panelled doors with chamfered fielded panels open to reveal nine narrow drawers. The case is supported on ogee bracket feet. The drawers show evidence of the early use to hold a butterfly collection. Rhode Island, circa 1770-1790.

Ht: 23″ Wd: 21½″ Dp: 19½″

A Miniature Gem

P-6344: Queen Anne curly maple miniature highboy. The drawers of the upper case are flanked by freestanding fluted columns. The boldly curved bandy cabriole legs integrate with the vibrantly scrolled apron to form a dramatic silhouette. Norwich, Connecticut or vicinity, circa 1760-1780.

Ex-collection Mrs. Ingersoll, Hartford, Connecticut

Ht: 32¾″ Wd: 17¾″ Dp: 9¾″

P-2664: Chippendale walnut claw and ball foot side chair. The horseshoe seat, turned stretchers and shell carved knees express the Queen Anne influence. The strapwork splat has scrolled terminals. Pleasing light brown patina. Newport, Rhode Island, circa 1760-1770.

Ht: 38½″

Ex-collection Israel Sack, Inc. and recently repurchased.

P-6377: Chippendale mahogany side chair with floral carving in crest center, molded terminals and interlaced splat. The seat is upholstered over the frame. The front cabriole legs, with sharp knees, terminate in well defined claw and ball feet with backswept side talons. Mellow brown color. Massachusetts, circa 1770-1780.

Ht: 36½″

P-6373: Chippendale walnut tripod dish top tea table with birdcage support, elliptical ball and ring turned pedestal with tapering shaft. Cabriole legs with good lift ending in platformed pad feet, fine old patina. Pennsylvania, circa 1760-1780.

Ht: 28½″ Diam: 31½″

P-6370: Hepplewhite birch tripod candlestand. The octagonal top is centered by a figured birch diamond panel and a diagonal checkered outer border. The beautifully modelled reeded pedestal is supported on bowed legs ending in spade feet. The legs have a floral ebonized black inlay. Portsmouth, New Hampshire, circa 1800-1810.

Ht: 28½″ Top: 21″ × 18″

P-4196: Chippendale mahogany block front bureau, bracket feet with spurred inner outline lobed center pendant, original brasses (except two lower handles), mellow light brown patina. Massachusetts, circa 1760-1780.

Ht: 31½″ Wd: 35¾″ Dp: 20¼″

History in drawer reads: "This bureau belonged to my grandfather, John Waldron of Boston, born 1799 also to his mother Sarah Hooten Waldron, who married General Joseph Warren. Elizabeth Warren Waldron, Somerville, Massachusetts June 24, 1930.

Illustrated in "American Antiques from Israel Sack Collection" Vol. V, pg. 1187 and recently repurchased.

P-5614: Queen Anne San Domingan mahogany porringer top tea table, flattened arch apron, turned legs ending in platformed pad feet, choice mellow brown patina, rare height adding to its usefulness as a tea table. Attributed to John Goddard, Newport, Rhode Island, circa 1740-1760.

Ht: 24″ Lg: ″ 36½ Wd: 22″

History:

Elizabeth Hodgson Hickling (1745-?) Duxbury, Massachusetts

Sarah B. Bradford, daughter, Duxbury, Massachusetts

Lucia, Elizabeth and Charlotte Bradford (their daughters), Duxbury, Massachusetts

Lucia Alden Bradford Knapp, Plymouth, Massachusetts, 1891

The maple cleats are secured to the top with rose headed nails and mortised into the sides to allow for expansion and contraction of the top. The name "Royal" seen in chalk indicates the ownership of Mrs. Royal, a previous owner, who was a Bradford.

P-3778: Empire mahogany sofa. The finely carved crest features a basket of fruit and brass chased mount in a star punch field with vine and grape carving. The crest, wings and seat have spiral carving. Made in Salem, Massachusetts, with carving attributed to Samuel Field McIntire, circa 1820-1835.

Ht: 38″ Wd: 78″ Dp: 23½″

P-6033: Pair of Classical "klismos" mahogany side chairs. The octagonal panels of the crests and splat feature floral carving. The molded stiles end in vigorous scrolled volutes. Massachusetts, circa 1810-1820.

Ht: 33″

Exhibited in Hirschl & Adler Galleries, Inc. exhibition entitled "Neo-Classicism in America: Inspiration and Innovation, 1810-1840" April-June 1991.

P-6393: Chippendale walnut bonnet top highboy. The lift of the cabriole legs, with ridged knees, combines with the triple ogee arches of the apron and the finely carved claw and ball feet to form a graceful silhouette. The drawers are made of richly grained walnut and retain the original Chippendale brasses. The center drawers of both the upper and lower case drawers are enhanced by fan carving. The flame finials are original (plinths restored). Fine mellow color and condition. Massachusetts, circa 1760-1780.

Ht: 7′ 3″ Wd: 39″ Dp: 21″

This highboy descended in the Bancroft family of Salem. A family inscription indicates its ownership by Ellen Julia Bancroft, born March 12, 1856.

Two highboys from Concord, Massachusetts, illustrated in ''New England Furniture'' by Jobe & Kaye, pgs. 205 and 206 exhibit aprons of the same form.

P-3802: Assembled set of six Queen Anne walnut side chairs, balloon seats, cabriole legs ending in pad feet, block and arrow turned stretchers, vase shaped splats, yoke shaped crest rails, light nut brown color. Massachusetts, circa 1740-1760. The chairs are well matched and show only slight variations.

Ex-collection Israel Sack, Inc. and recently repurchased.

P-1146: Queen Anne mahogany square tilt top table. The one board top, with molded edges, is made of richly grained highly figured crotch mahogany. The tapered column, with medial bulbous vase turning, connects the tripod base of three cabriole legs with ridged bulbous pad feet on raised pads. The exceptionally beautiful wood used in such an effective manner in the top, the strength of the cabriole legs and the successful overall proportions make this table a truly rare example. Massachusetts, circa 1750-1770.

Ht: 28″ Top: 35″

Illustrated in ''American Antiques from Israel Sack Collection'' Vol. I, pg. 270 and recently repurchased.

P-6369: Pair of Chinese paintings on board depicting scenes of the Pear River in China. The first portrays a boat with Chinese lanterns, houses, people and trees in a river and landscaped setting; the second a gazebo on a projecting cliff above a river with mountains in the background. In fine condition. Chinese, circa 1800-1815.

Ht: 21½″ Wd: 26 5/8″

P-5518: Queen Anne mahogany drop-leaf table of desirable large size. The graceful cabriole legs have voluted knee brackets and platformed pad feet. The end aprons are double cyma shaped. Deep color and mellow patina. Massachusetts, circa 1750-1770.

Ht: 27½″ Lg: 60″ Wd: open 59″ closed 19″

Illustrated in "American Antiques from Israel Sack Collection" Vol. VIII, pg. 2074 and recently repurchased.

P-5569: Chippendale mahogany and gilt ''Constitution'' mirror. The original carved and gilded phoenix ornament is sculptured perfection. The original carved and gilded side leaves, frame borders, crest molding ending in sunflower carved capitals retain the original gilding. American or English, circa 1760-1780.

Ht: 84″ Wd: 26″

Illustrated in ''American Antiques from Israel Sack Collection'' Vol. VIII, pg. 2084 and recently repurchased.

P-6384: Chippendale mahogany oxbow bureau with finely sculptured claw and ball feet and important original willow brasses. The compact proportions, the choice figured grain and beautiful golden patina enhance the beauty of the piece. Massachusetts, circa 1760-1780.

Ht: 31¾″ Wd: 35¼″ Dp: 20½″

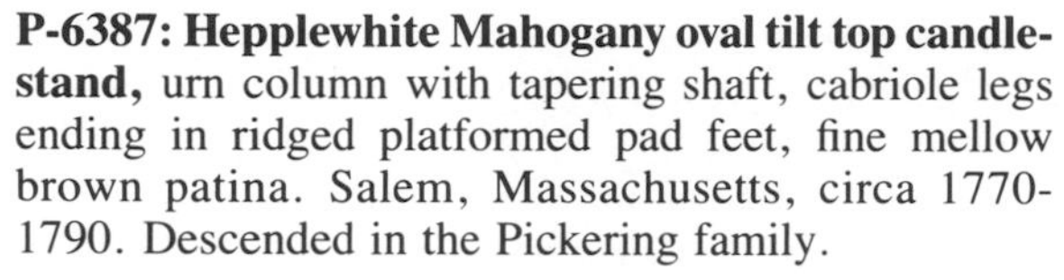

P-6387: Hepplewhite Mahogany oval tilt top candlestand, urn column with tapering shaft, cabriole legs ending in ridged platformed pad feet, fine mellow brown patina. Salem, Massachusetts, circa 1770-1790. Descended in the Pickering family.

Ht: 28¼″ Top: 15½″ × 21¼″

P-4086: Chippendale cherry tripod tilt-top dish top candlestand. The elliptical ball and ring turned pedestal has a fluted tapering shaft, a rare and desirable feature. The table has acquired a beautiful amber patina. Philadelphia, circa 1760-1780.

Ht: 28″ Diam: 17½″

Illustrated in "Fine Points of Furniture Early American" pg. 257.

Illustrated in "American Antiques from Israel Sack Collection" Vol V, pg. 1233 and recently repurchased.

P-2717: Queen Anne mahogany lowboy. The upper full width drawer is above three deeper lower drawers, the central one of which is deeply carved with a concave shell with scribed borders. Graceful cabriole legs, with scrolled bracket returns, rest on pad feet with raised wafers. Deep mellow brown color. Massachusetts, circa 1740-1760.

Ht: 30¼″ Wd: 34″ Dp: 20¾″

Ex-collection Israel Sack, Inc, and recently repurchased.

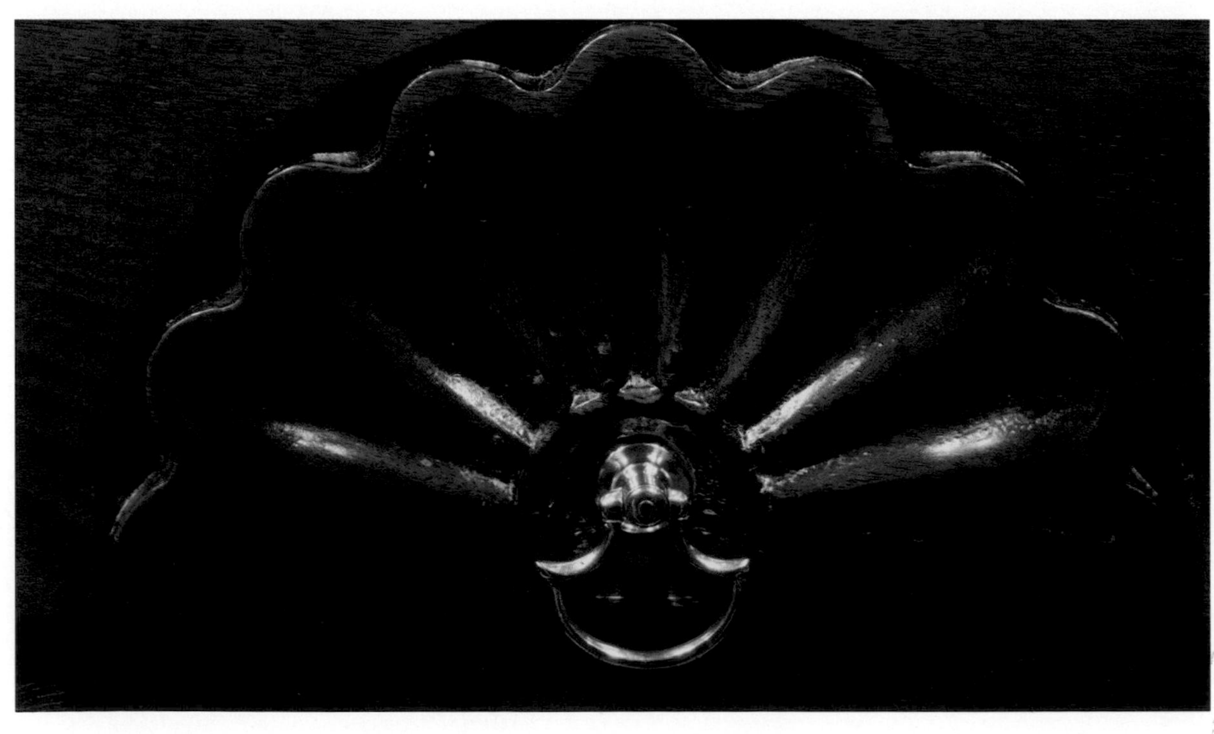

P-2610: Chippendale mahogany tripod dish top bridcage candlestand with claw and ball feet, elliptical ball and ring column and crisply carved claw and ball feet. One foot is an old replacement. This is one of the finest stands we have ever owned. Philadelphia, circa 1760-1780.

Ht: 29″ Diam: 23½″

Ex-collection Israel Sack, Inc. and recently repurchased.

P-6364: Queen Anne mahogany tilt-top candlestand. The oval top rests on a turned and tapered column connecting the tripod base of three cabriole legs terminating in ridged bulbous pad feet. Massachusetts, circa 1780-1790.

Ht: 27″ Wd: 20¾″ × 15½″

P-5145: Queen Anne walnut and maple lowboy of diminutive scale and beautiful proportions. The sides and graceful cabriole legs are maple. The cleated sides of the molded top is a rare feature that indicates an early date. Salem, Massachusetts or vicinity, circa 1740-1750.

Ht: 29¼″ Wd: 33¼″ Dp: 20½″

Illustrated in ''American Antiques from Israel Sack Collection'' Vol. VII, pg. 1849 and recently repurchased.

P-3470: Pair of Sheraton mahogany side chairs. The central splat with drapery and plume carving, tapered legs with beaded borders ending in spade feet. New York, circa 1800-1810.

Ht: 36½″

Illustrated in ''American Antiques from Israel Sack Collection'' Vol. III, pg. 805 and recently repurchased.

P-6306: Brass bust of Lafayette, on molded marble base. French for the American market, circa 1810-1830.

Ht: 11½″

P-6363: Sheraton marble and gilt Bilboa mirror. The marble columns, set against the black background of the frame is an attractive variation. Finely festooned crest with urn and wheat stalk central ornament. Original gilt and glass. Continental for the American market, circa 1800-1810.

Ht: 42″ Wd: 17″

Ex-collection Francis Hill Bigelow

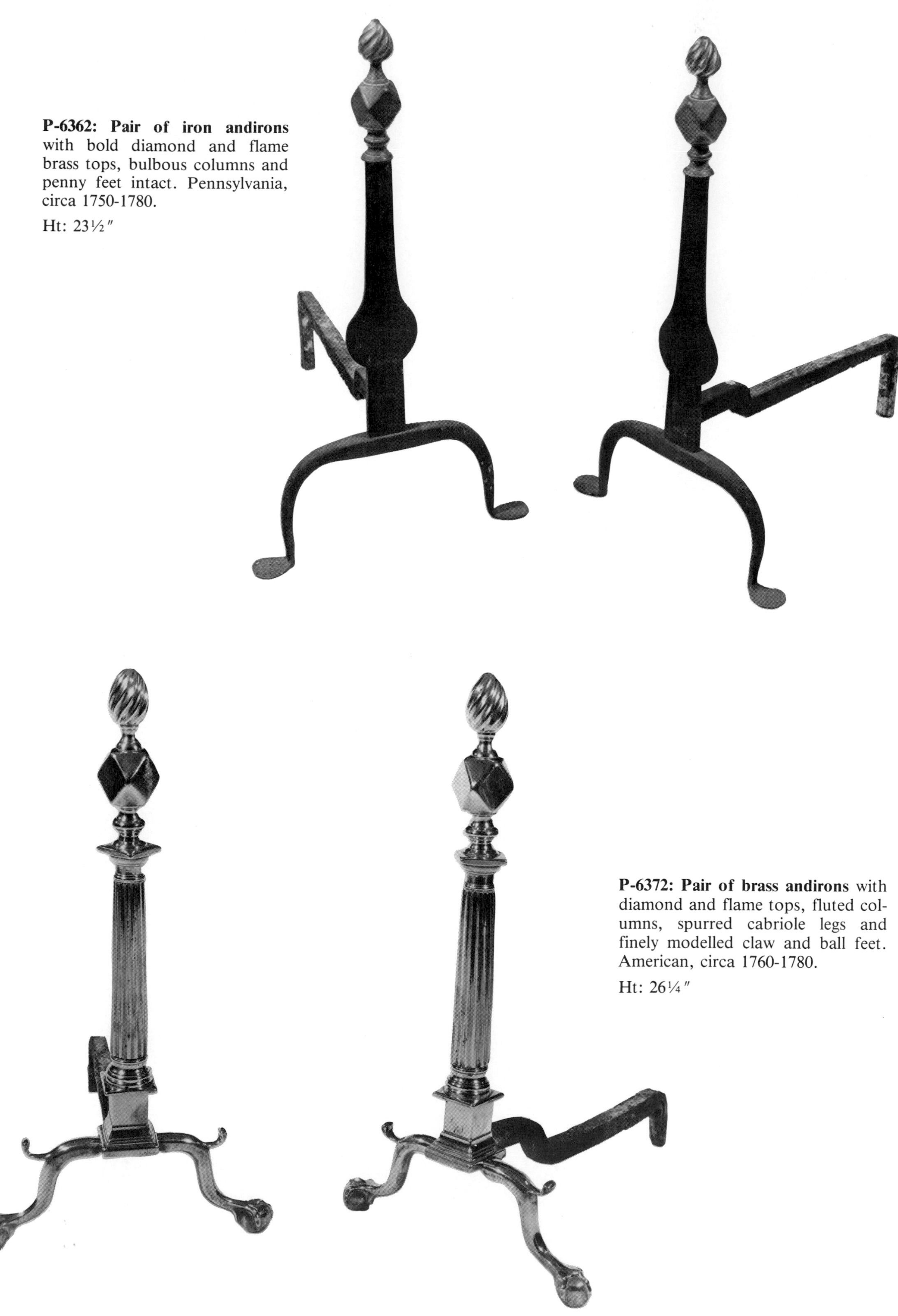

P-6362: Pair of iron andirons with bold diamond and flame brass tops, bulbous columns and penny feet intact. Pennsylvania, circa 1750-1780.

Ht: 23½″

P-6372: Pair of brass andirons with diamond and flame tops, fluted columns, spurred cabriole legs and finely modelled claw and ball feet. American, circa 1760-1780.

Ht: 26¼″

P-2465: Sheraton mahogany side chair. The splat is of lattice formation with connecting square rosettes. The raised crest panel has repeat drapery carving in star punch or snowflake background. School of Samuel McIntire, Salem, Massachusetts, circa 1800-1810.

Ht: 37″

A chair of the same design, but with stretchers, is available.

Ex-collection Israel Sack, Inc. and recently repurchased.

P-850: Sheraton mahogany armchair. The central splat features a carved drapery and plume. This New England interpretation of the more prevalent New York version has thumbnail notching on the uprights supporting the drapery. The plain incurvate arms and supports and the tapered molded legs support the Massachusetts origin. Circa 1800-1810. Fine nut brown patina.

Ht: 35½″ Wd: 20¼″

Illustrated in "American Antiques from Israel Sack Collection" Vol. IV, pg. 1076 and recently repurchased.

P-6383: Sheraton gilt "tabernacle" mirror. The original glass and eglomise panel are flanked by concave columns with spherules. The panel depicts charming landscape waterfront scene with animals and a lady with parasol. Boston, Massachusetts, circa 1800-1815.

Ht: 39″ Wd: 23½″

P-6342: Sheraton gilt "tabernacle" mirror. The glass and panel are flanked by twin reeded columns with spiral bead center. The original eglomise glass panel features an urn with leaf branches in a lime green background. Boston, Massachusetts, circa 1800-1810.

Ht: 43¾″ Wd: 21¼″

P-3459: Rare matched pair of Sheraton mahogany work tables. The rectangular tops join ringed turrets above star-punched legs with grapevine carving in relief and reeding on the swelled and tapering lower sections. The cases house divided upper drawers and lower bag drawers, both fronted with richly grained crotch mahogany veneer which is repeated on the sides and backs. One with original brass knobs. The fine quality of these tables is further enhanced by the distinction of being a matched pair. School of Samuel McIntire. Massachusetts, circa 1790-1810.

Ht: 29″ Wd: 22¾″ Dp: 17¼″

Ex-collection Israel Sack, Inc. and recently repurchased.

P-4218: Pair of Hepplewhite mahogany shield back side chairs, the splats of each artistically fashioned with a solid central urn supporting a carved drapery supported by scrolls and framed in a leaf carved oval, fine golden patina. Connecticut, circa 1780-1800.

Ht: 39″

A chair of this design is illustrated in "American Furniture of the Federal Period" by Charles Montgomery, plate 47.

Illustrated in "American Antiques from Israel Sack Collection" Vol. V, pg. 1295 and recently repurchased.

P-5432: Classical mahogany tambour work table. The case with astragal ends exhibits the choice veneered patterns associated with Phyfe's superior handiwork, the top with reeded edge reveals a writing compartment. Reeded column and molded outsplayed legs. Duncan Phyfe or a contemporary of equal rank, New York circa 1810-1820.

Ht: 30¼″ Wd: 25¼″ Dp: 13″

Illustrated in ''American Antiques from Israel Sack Collection'' Vol. VII, pg. 2050 and recently repurchased.

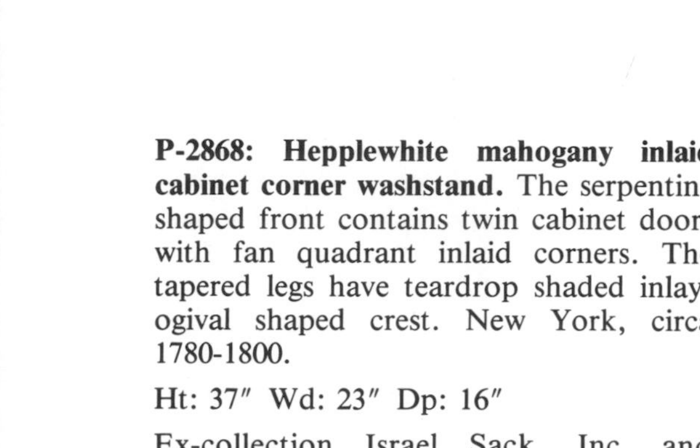

P-2868: Hepplewhite mahogany inlaid cabinet corner washstand. The serpentine shaped front contains twin cabinet doors with fan quadrant inlaid corners. The tapered legs have teardrop shaded inlay, ogival shaped crest. New York, circa 1780-1800.

Ht: 37″ Wd: 23″ Dp: 16″

Ex-collection Israel Sack, Inc. and recently repurchased.

P-5401: Sheraton mahogany inlaid secretary-desk, the base with three drawers flanked by reeded columns supported on tapered reeded legs. The upper case with Gothic mullioned glass doors crested by leafy scrolls in silhouette. The drawers and plinth panels are bordered by satinwood crossbanding. Fine mellow brown patina. Boston, Massachusetts, circa 1800-1815.

Ht: 80½″ Wd: 37″ Dp: 22½″

Illustrated in ''American Antiques from Israel Sack Collection'' Vol. VII, pg 2036 and recently repurchased.

P-5496: Set of six Hepplewhite mahogany shield back side chairs, finely carved splats of drapery and bellflower design. The bold sweep of the serpentine seat, the shape of the shield and the exposed mortise of the rear stile distinguish this form from the more prevalent related New York variety. In a fine state of preservation. Newport, Rhode Island, circa 1780-1800.

Ht: 40″

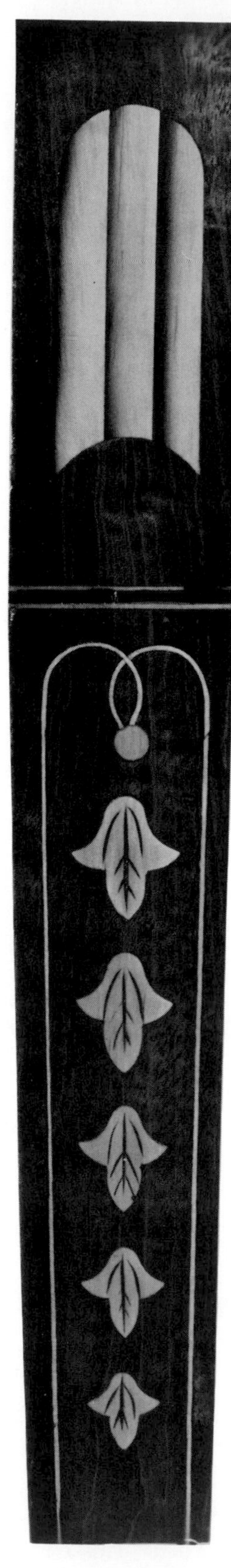

P-2165: Hepplewhite mahogany pembroke table with finely grained top with thumb molded edge. The bowed frames, one of which houses a drawer, are flanked by tapered legs with arched book inlay above line inlaid panels of bellflowers of descending size and light wood cuffs. Attributed to John Townsend, Newport, Rhode Island (See: "Master Craftsmen of Newport" Moses & Sack, fig. 2.11, pg. 83) circa 1785-1795.

Ht: 28″ Wd: 38″ open, 18½″ closed

Ex-collection Israel Sack, Inc. and recently re-purchased.

P-5576: Sheraton mahogany sofa with incurvate arms and three paneled crest, the center panel drapery carved, the end panels carved with reeds and bowknot motifs, the bold serpentine arms have a reeded facade, reeded acanthus carved arm supports, reeded seat frame, tapered reeded legs ending in bulbous castered feet. Made by Duncan Phyfe or a contemporary of equal rank. New York, circa 1800-1825.

Ht: 37″ Lg: 6′ 8″ Dp: 32″

Illustrated in ''American Antiques from Israel Sack Collection'' Vol. VIII, pg. 2213 and recently repurchased.

For a related sofa see ''American Furniture — The Federal Period'' Montgomery, No. 277, pg. 310.

P-6390: Pair of Bilsted enamel mirror knobs. The scene depicts the first successful balloon ascension in America. The ascension was made by Jean P. Blanchard at Philadelphia January 9, 1793. English for the American market, circa 1800-1810.

Ht: 1 7/8″ Wd: 7/8″

P-5797: Sheraton gilt mirror with original eglomise glass panel depicting a house with river with sailing ship and landscape beyond. The gilded frame has spherules at the cornice and cluster columns surmounted by acanthus capitals. The mirror bears the original engraved label of John Doggett, Roxbury, Massachusetts, circa 1800-1820.

Ht: 41½″ Wd: 21½″

P-2289: Miniature banjo clock with watch movement. The original eglomise panels are floral in a white background with checkered inlaid borders. The brass finial served as a winding key for the watch behind the brass dial. The period watch behind the dial is not original to the case. Willard school, Boston, Massachusetts, circa 1800-1815.

Ht: 16¾″ Wd: 5″

Illustrated in "American Antiques from Israel Sack Collection" Vol. II, pg. 337 and recently repurchased.

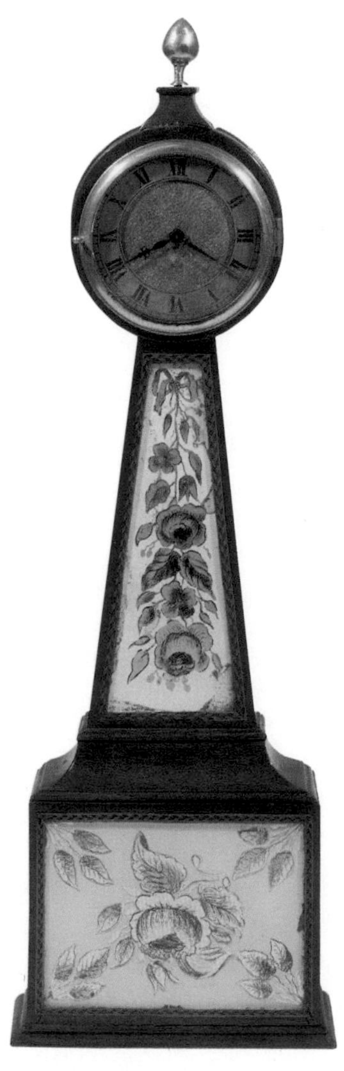

P-6352: Classical gilt convex mirror of rare small size. The circular frame has a deep coved molding ornamented with spherules and is flanked by leaf shaped wings. The frame is surmounted by a finely sculptured eagle poised for flight on a broad leaf mounting with corresponding leafage at the base. New York or English, circa 1810-1820.

Ht: 35″ Wd: 16½

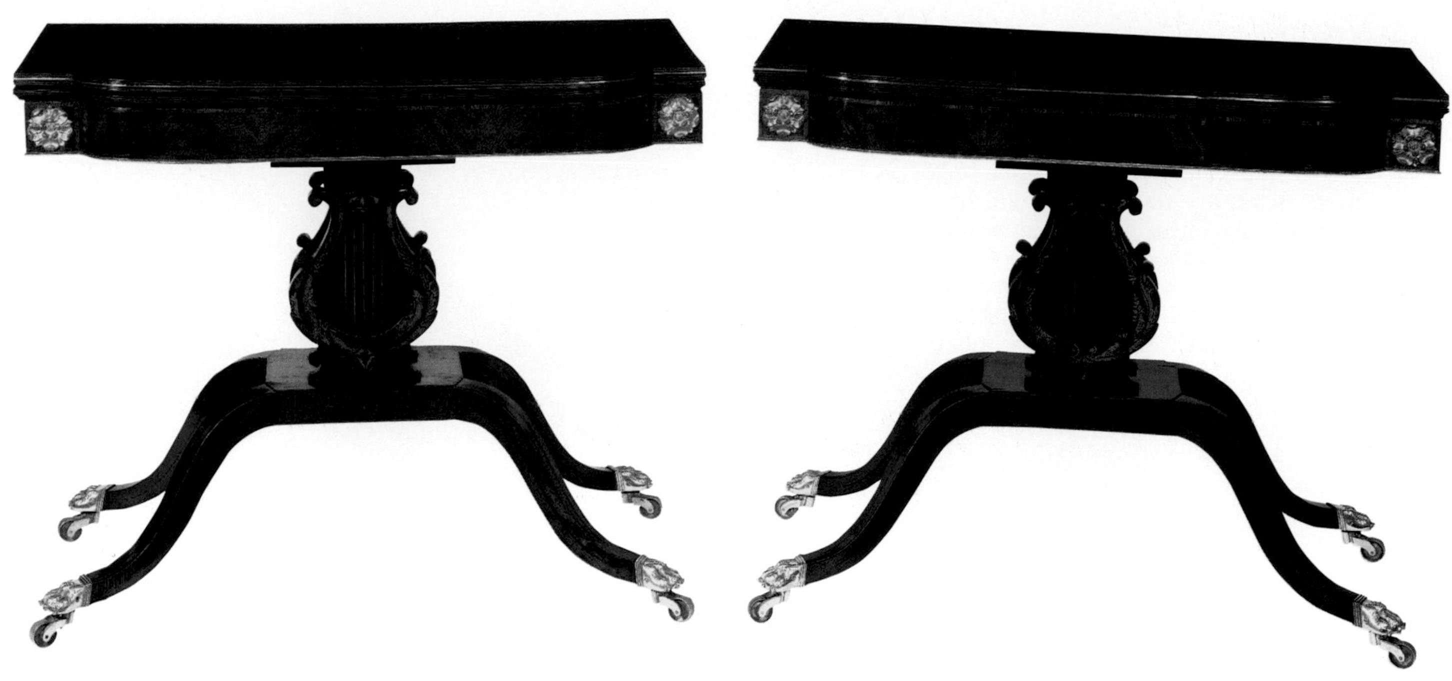

P-6085: Pair of Classical lyre base card tables. The lyres have stencilled decoration of leaves and star motifs. The sinuous cabriole legs have gilt paint with black stripes. The plinths of the frames have brass petalled mounts. Massachusetts, circa 1810-1820.

Ht: 30½″ Wd: 36″ Dp: 18″

P-6341: Set of four Classical chairs of klismos form with painted decoration. The decoration is gilt with green striping in a creamy white background. The caned seats each front a floral panel. The chairs are each branded HOLDEN'S. Boston, Massachusetts, circa 1810-1830. Joshua Holden is listed as a chairmaker on Washington and Orange Streets, Boston, 1810-1835.

Ht: 35″

P-4825: Hepplewhite mahogany bow front bureau. The overhanging top is line-inlaid along the outer edges. The drawers, with beaded borders, are enhanced by finely grained mahogany, cut-cornered line inlay and original oval pulls and escutcheons. The double cyma shaped front apron with patterned inlay above, joins tall French splayed feet. Massachusetts, circa 1780-1800.

Ht: 37½″ Wd: 40½″ Dp: 21½″

Ex-collection Israel Sack, Inc. and recently repurchased.

P-5741: Pair of Hepplewhite mahogany side chairs. The molded shield backs house three shaped members which join inlaid quarter fans at the bottom of the shields. One chair is branded SF for Samuel Fiske, cabinet and chair maker. Salem, Massachusetts, circa 1780-1795. Warm faded brown color.

Ht: 37¾″

P-6218: Chippendale mahogany and gilt mirror with finely scrolled crest and base. The scroll-board features a phoenix silhouetted in circle flanked by graceful trailing vines. A gilt pressed shell centers the base. The mirror retains the original glass and backboard. Massachusetts or English, circa 1770-1780.

Ht: 42½″ Wd: 18¼

Descended in the family of Dr. Russell of Massachusetts

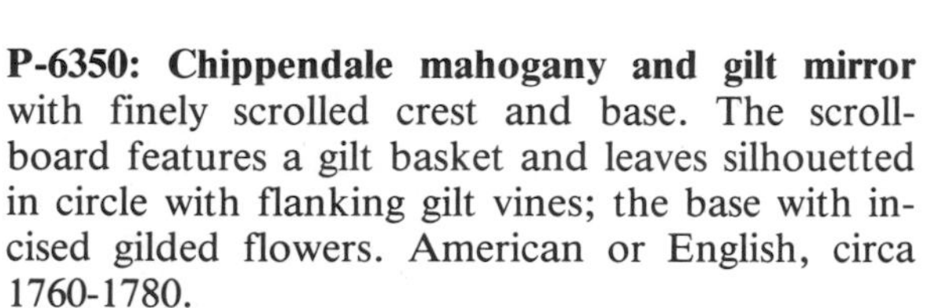

P-6350: Chippendale mahogany and gilt mirror with finely scrolled crest and base. The scroll-board features a gilt basket and leaves silhouetted in circle with flanking gilt vines; the base with incised gilded flowers. American or English, circa 1760-1780.

Ht: 45″ Wd: 20¼″

P-3514: Assembled pair of Hepplewhite mahogany demilune card tables with leaf carved tapered legs, crescent fluted top borders and gadrooned aprons made by Stephen Badlam, Dorchester, Massachusetts, circa 1790-1800. An identical table branded S. Badlam is illustrated in ''Antiques'' Magazine, December 1931, pg. 339.

Ht: 28½″ Wd: 36″ Dp: 17½

Illustrated in ''American Antiques from Israel Sack Collection'' Vol. III, pg. 829 and recently repurchased.

P-6389: Hepplewhite mahogany inlaid serpentine front sideboard. This example is typical of a group of New York sideboards that are considered the acme of American achievement in the sideboard form. The features are the canted center legs which have a knife blade effect and the recessed center cupboard which relieves any tendency for bulk. Both features, plus the richly figured veneers and the fine inlaid patterns, result in a highly successful composition. New York, circa, 1780-1800.

Ht: 42″ Wd: 72″ Dp: 29¼″

P-6386: Sheraton birdseye maple canterbury. The arched crests are supported by vertical slats on all four sides, while the solid divider has a cut-out handgrip. The case contains one drawer and is supported on delicate turned castered legs. New York, circa 1800-1810.

Ht: 20½″ Wd: 18″ Dp: 13¼″

P-6375: Rare small Windsor settee. The bow crest, typical of Philadelphia, rests on the back rail which continues to molded and scrolled handholds. Turned arm supports cant from the seat to the arm and front bamboo turned spindles. The splayed legs and the stretchers are correspondingly turned and nicely tapered. Old black paint with yellow accent ring scoring. Philadelphia, circa 1780-1800.

Ht: 32¾″ Wd: 32½″ Dp: 15½

P-6361: Rare large pair of gilded tin eagles fitted with holders for flares. In fine state of preservation. Circa 1850.

Ht: 19″ Wd: 38″

P-6348: Rare paktong inkstand. A circular dished tray marked E.C. on footed base is complete with covered sander and inkwell, candleholders and bell. Paktong is a rare metal produced in England for a short period to simulate silver. To our knowledge, an inkstand of this quality in this metal is rare or unique. The Winterthur laboratories have confirmed the paktong composition. English, circa 1780-1800.

Ht: 10″ Tray diam: 9 5/8″

P-3307: Classical gilt harp made and signed by Browne and Buckwell, Makers, New York. That partnership was active in New York between 1870 and 1878. American made harps are quite rare. An example by this maker is in the Metropolitan Museum of Art.

Ht: 67½″ Wd: 20″ Dp: 32″

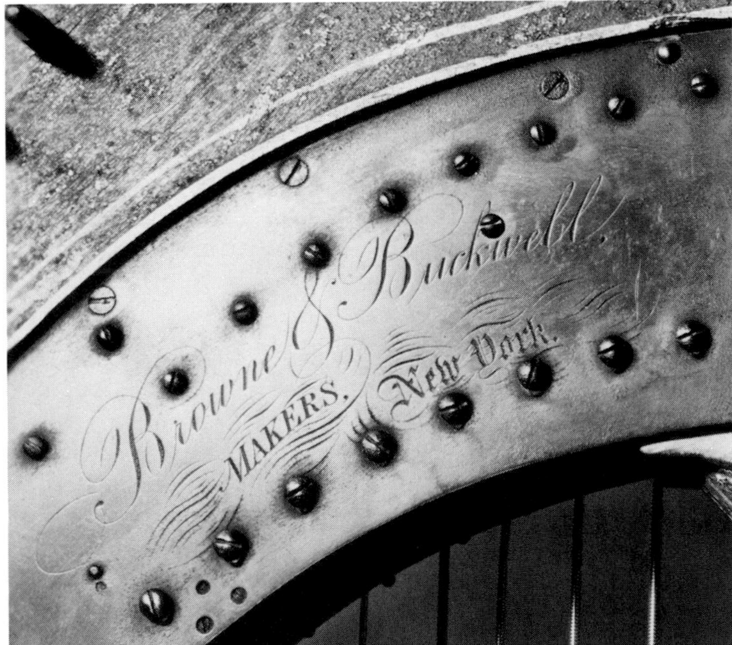

P-5752: Classical mahogany card table with mechanical swing leg mechanism, top with finely figured crotch veneer. The acanthus carved urn column is supported by acanthus carved outsplayed legs. Attributed to Duncan Phyfe or a contemporary of equal rank. New York, circa 1810-1820.

Ht: 29″ Wd: 36½″ Dp: 18″

Illustrated in "American Antiques from Israel Sack Collection" Vol. VIII, pg. 2259 and recently repurchased.

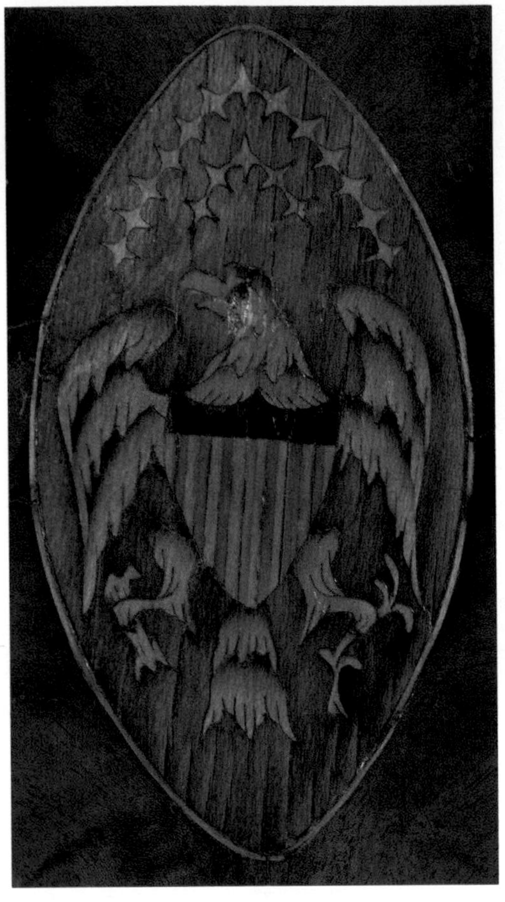

P-6346: Hepplewhite mahogany and gilt mirror of important size. The scrollboard features an inlaid oval patera symbolizing the New Republic (eagle, shield and 18 stars). The bold acanthus carved urn ornament with leaf sprays is complemented by equally bold floral and leaf carved side vines. The original eglomise panel depicts a maritime scene. The mirror retains the original glass and gilding. New York, circa 1800-1815.

Ht: 66½″ Wd: 24¼″

P-4185: Sheraton mahogany card table with bowed front and serpentine sides. The edges of the tops have double line diagonal inlay; the aprons are divided by rectangular panels of satinwood veneer and the frontal plinths are inlaid with beautifully detailed elongated floral motifs. The turned and tapered legs with cylindrical collars are enhanced by rare inlaid satinwood panels which conform to the legs taper. Rich mellow color. Salem, Massachusetts, circa 1800-1810.

Ht: 28¾″ Wd: 39″ Dp: 18″

Illustrated in "American Antiques from Israel Sack Collection" Vol. V, pg. 1242 and recently repurchased.

P-4603: Sheraton mahogany sofa with center paneled back. The raised panel with reeded coved ends contains a carved drapery joined by carved rings and tassels. The back and graceful arms are framed with beaded-edged mahogany which joins the arm supports and plinths of the two outer front legs. The four front legs are turned and tapered above spade feet on brass casters. Massachusetts, circa 1795-1805.

Ht: 40½″ Lg: 6′ 5¼″ Dp: 28½″

Illustrated in "American Antiques from Israel Sack Collection" Vol. VI, pg. 1551 and recently repurchased.

John Elliott.

AT his Looking-Glaſs Store, the Sign of the Bell and Looking-Glaſs, in Street *Philadelphia* *Imports* and ſells all Sorts of Engliſh Looking-Glaſses at the loweſt Rates.

He alſo new Quickſilvers and frames old Glaſses, and ſupply's People with new Glaſs to their own Frames.

Dſchan Elliott

WOhnhaft zu Philadelphia in der Straß, wo ein Schild heraus hangt zur Belle und Spiegel, hat ein Stoor und groſſen Vorrath von allerley engliſchen Spiegeln, und verkauft ſie vor den niedrigſten Preiß.

ihre alte Rahmen.

P-4234: Queen Anne mahogany mirror of important size bearing the original label of John Elliott in German and English. The molded frame has carved and gilded inner borders. The scrolled crest contains a carved and gilded shell in silhouette. The two section bevelled glasses are old but may not be original to the mirror. Philadelphia or English, circa 1740-1770.

Ht: 57″ Wd: 20½″

P-6385: Queen Anne walnut side chair, rectangular seat with scalloped front apron. A chair of the finest connoisseur quality in the original condition including finish. Massachusetts, circa 1740-1760.

Ht: 40¼″

P-6353: Rare Hepplewhite mahogany inlaid corner table. The serpentine front frame is inlaid in diamond and pellet pattern with a checkered inlaid apron border. The bulbous turned slender legs are surmounted by plinths with oval paterae. Maryland, circa 1800-1810.

Ht: 33″ Wd: 28″ Dp: 18¾″

P-6360: Sheraton mahogany armchair. The central splat features a drapery and plume carved open urn with fan carved spandrel corners, beautifully modelled serpentine arms with carved rosette terminals, reeded legs ending in spade feet. New York, circa 1800-1810. A chair of the finest quality and finish.

Ht: 36″ Wd: 21½″

P-4360: Sheraton mahogany armchair. The central splat features a drapery and plume carved open urn with fan carved spandrel corners, beautifully modelled serpentine arms with carved rosette terminals, reeded legs ending in spade feet. New York, circa 1800-1810. A chair of the finest quality and finish

Ht: 34½″ Dp: 23″

Ex-collection C.K. Davis

Illustrated in "American Antiques from Israel Sack Collection" Vol. V, pg. 1348 and recently repurchased.

P-5095: Sheraton mahogany sofa with three panel carved crest rail. The center panel of ribbon drapery and tassel carving is flanked on either side by fluted panels. Slender tapered reeded legs ending in bulbous castered feet. Attributed to Duncan Phyfe or a contemporary of equal rank. New York, circa 1800-1810.

Ht: 36¾″ Wd: 78″ Dp: 33″

P-2736: Sheraton mahogany end table. The rectangular frame has canted corners and contains one drawer with ivory inlaid escutcheon. The delicate reeded tapered legs have leaf carved capitals and pear shaped bulbous feet. The sides and rear have beaded outlined panels and the top has twin reeded edges. Salem, Massachusetts, circa 1800-1810.

Ht: 27¼″ Wd: 18″ Dp: 18″

Illustrated in ''American Antiques from Israel Sack Collection'' Vol. II, pg 499 and recently repurchased.

P-2544: Sheraton mahogany sewing table. The rectangular frame contains one drawer. The sewing slide at one side retains the original partial label of Jacob Forster, Charlestown, Massachusetts dated 1814. The drawer is flanked by fluted plinths and the top has a quarter round ''thumbnail'' border.

Ht: 27″ Wd: 20″ Dp: 14″

Illustrated in ''American Antiques from Israel Sack Collection'' Vol. II, pg. 498 and recently repurchased.

INDEX

This index is for all ten volumes of *American Antiques From Israel Sack Collection*. It is arranged in the following order.

FIRST:	Listed alphabetically by item (i.e. "BEDS", "BELLOWS", "BOWLS", etc.)
SECOND:	These items are individually arranged in order by period. (i.e., "Early" followed by "Pilgrim", "William & Mary", etc.)
THIRD:	Within each period, numbers preceded by a "p." are page numbers, any numbers following the page number are photo numbers. (i.e., "p. 874, 3228 low post;" refers to page number 874, photo number 3228)

The sequence of page numbers through the complete set of ten volumes is as follows:

Volume 1	pages	1	-	289
Volume 2	pages	293	-	581
Volume 3	pages	585	-	847
Volume 4	pages	852	-	1112
Volume 5	pages	1116	-	1387
Volume 6	pages	1437	-	1687
Volume 7	pages	1689	-	2061
Volume 8	pages	2062	-	2385
Volume 9	pages	2386	-	2541
Volume 10	pages	2542	-	2721

INDEX

CHAIRS, SLIPPER

CHAIRS, WING

CHAIRS, WINDOW

CHANDELIER

CHESTS

TABLES, SIDEBOARD

TABLES, SOFA

TABLES, TAVERN

TABLES, TEA

TABLES, TIP

TABLES, TRESTLE

TABLES, TRIPOD

TABLES, TRIPOD; CANDLESTANDS

TABLES, TUCKAWAY

TABLES, WORK

TABLES, WRITING

TAPE LOOM

THERMOMETER

TORCHERE

TRAYS